The Migraine Journal
© 2022 by Emma Roberts

All rights reserved. No part of this publication may be reproduced, distributed, or transmitted in any form or by any means, including photocopying, recording, or other electronic or mechanical methods, without the prior written permission of the publisher, except in the case of brief quotations embodied in critical reviews and certain other noncommercial uses permitted by copyright law.

Printed in the United States of America
First Printing, 2022.
ISBN 978-1-938249-21-1 (paperback)

Cover design by BookCoverZone.com

Date:_____ Time:_____

How long did the headache last:_____

How severe is the pain? (Circle a number)

1   2   3   4   5   6   7   8   9   10

Warning signs (hours to days prior)?

- Mood change
- Decreased concentration
- Visual disturbance
- Physical symptoms
- Fatigue
- Sensitivity to light, sounds, or smells
- Neck discomfort
- Difficult speaking/reading
- Nausea
- Change in bowel habits
- Food cravings/thirst
- Yawning
- Other:_____

Headache symptoms?

- Pain on one side
- Pain on both sides
- Throbbing pain
- Constant pain
- Sensitive to light
- Sensitive to sound
- Worse with movement
- Nausea/vomiting
- Nasal congestion
- Feeling cold or warm
- Sensitive to smell/touch
- Neck pain
- Visual or other physical symptoms
- Other:_____

Potential triggers?

- Diet change
- Change in water/caffeine/alcohol intake
- Decreased sleep
- Medication change
- Increased stress
- Weather
- Amount of light
- Strong smells
- Loud sounds
- Hormone change
- Pressure on head
- Vitamin/mineral deficiency
- Change in exercise
- Travel
- Other:_____

Feelings afterward?

- Feel normal
- Depressed
- Very happy
- Fatigued
- Decreased concentration
- Other:_____

Additional details of headache:

Date:_____ Time:_____

How long did the headache last:_____

How severe is the pain? (Circle a number)

1 2 3 4 5 6 7 8 9 10

Warning signs (hours to days prior)?

- ○ Mood change
- ○ Decreased concentration
- ○ Visual disturbance
- ○ Physical symptoms
- ○ Fatigue
- ○ Sensitivity to light, sounds, or smells
- ○ Neck discomfort
- ○ Difficult speaking/reading
- ○ Nausea
- ○ Change in bowel habits
- ○ Food cravings/thirst
- ○ Yawning
- ○ Other:_____

Headache symptoms?

- ○ Pain on one side
- ○ Pain on both sides
- ○ Throbbing pain
- ○ Constant pain
- ○ Sensitive to light
- ○ Sensitive to sound
- ○ Worse with movement
- ○ Nausea/vomiting
- ○ Nasal congestion
- ○ Feeling cold or warm
- ○ Sensitive to smell/touch
- ○ Neck pain
- ○ Visual or other physical symptoms
- ○ Other:_____

Potential triggers?

- ○ Diet change
- ○ Change in water/caffeine/alcohol intake
- ○ Decreased sleep
- ○ Medication change
- ○ Increased stress
- ○ Weather
- ○ Amount of light
- ○ Strong smells
- ○ Loud sounds
- ○ Hormone change
- ○ Pressure on head
- ○ Vitamin/mineral deficiency
- ○ Change in exercise
- ○ Travel
- ○ Other:_____

Feelings afterward?

- ○ Feel normal
- ○ Depressed
- ○ Very happy
- ○ Fatigued
- ○ Decreased concentration
- ○ Other:_____

Additional details of headache:

Date:_____ Time:_____

How long did the headache last:_____

How severe is the pain? (Circle a number)

1 2 3 4 5 6 7 8 9 10

Warning signs (hours to days prior)?

- Mood change
- Decreased concentration
- Visual disturbance
- Physical symptoms
- Fatigue
- Sensitivity to light, sounds, or smells
- Neck discomfort
- Difficult speaking/reading
- Nausea
- Change in bowel habits
- Food cravings/thirst
- Yawning
- Other:_____

Headache symptoms?

- Pain on one side
- Pain on both sides
- Throbbing pain
- Constant pain
- Sensitive to light
- Sensitive to sound
- Worse with movement
- Nausea/vomiting
- Nasal congestion
- Feeling cold or warm
- Sensitive to smell/touch
- Neck pain
- Visual or other physical symptoms
- Other:_____

Potential triggers?

- Diet change
- Change in water/caffeine/alcohol intake
- Decreased sleep
- Medication change
- Increased stress
- Weather
- Amount of light
- Strong smells
- Loud sounds
- Hormone change
- Pressure on head
- Vitamin/mineral deficiency
- Change in exercise
- Travel
- Other:_____

Feelings afterward?

- Feel normal
- Depressed
- Very happy
- Fatigued
- Decreased concentration
- Other:_____

Additional details of headache:

Date:_____ Time:_____

How long did the headache last:_____

How severe is the pain? (Circle a number)

1   2   3   4   5   6   7   8   9   10

Warning signs (hours to days prior)?

- Mood change
- Decreased concentration
- Visual disturbance
- Physical symptoms
- Fatigue
- Sensitivity to light, sounds, or smells
- Neck discomfort
- Difficult speaking/reading
- Nausea
- Change in bowel habits
- Food cravings/thirst
- Yawning
- Other:_____

Headache symptoms?

- Pain on one side
- Pain on both sides
- Throbbing pain
- Constant pain
- Sensitive to light
- Sensitive to sound
- Worse with movement
- Nausea/vomiting
- Nasal congestion
- Feeling cold or warm
- Sensitive to smell/touch
- Neck pain
- Visual or other physical symptoms
- Other:_____

Potential triggers?

- Diet change
- Change in water/caffeine/alcohol intake
- Decreased sleep
- Medication change
- Increased stress
- Weather
- Amount of light
- Strong smells
- Loud sounds
- Hormone change
- Pressure on head
- Vitamin/mineral deficiency
- Change in exercise
- Travel
- Other:_____

Feelings afterward?

- Feel normal
- Depressed
- Very happy
- Fatigued
- Decreased concentration
- Other:_____

Additional details of headache:

Date:_____ Time:_____

How long did the headache last:_____

How severe is the pain? (Circle a number)

1　2　3　4　5　6　7　8　9　10

Warning signs (hours to days prior)?

- Mood change
- Decreased concentration
- Visual disturbance
- Physical symptoms
- Fatigue
- Sensitivity to light, sounds, or smells
- Neck discomfort
- Difficult speaking/reading
- Nausea
- Change in bowel habits
- Food cravings/thirst
- Yawning
- Other:_____

Headache symptoms?

- Pain on one side
- Pain on both sides
- Throbbing pain
- Constant pain
- Sensitive to light
- Sensitive to sound
- Worse with movement
- Nausea/vomiting
- Nasal congestion
- Feeling cold or warm
- Sensitive to smell/touch
- Neck pain
- Visual or other physical symptoms
- Other:_____

Potential triggers?

- Diet change
- Change in water/caffeine/alcohol intake
- Decreased sleep
- Medication change
- Increased stress
- Weather
- Amount of light
- Strong smells
- Loud sounds
- Hormone change
- Pressure on head
- Vitamin/mineral deficiency
- Change in exercise
- Travel
- Other:_____

Feelings afterward?

- Feel normal
- Depressed
- Very happy
- Fatigued
- Decreased concentration
- Other:_____

Additional details of headache:

Date:_____ Time:_____

How long did the headache last:_____

How severe is the pain? (Circle a number)

1 2 3 4 5 6 7 8 9 10

Warning signs (hours to days prior)?

- Mood change
- Decreased concentration
- Visual disturbance
- Physical symptoms
- Fatigue
- Sensitivity to light, sounds, or smells
- Neck discomfort
- Difficult speaking/reading
- Nausea
- Change in bowel habits
- Food cravings/thirst
- Yawning
- Other:_____

Headache symptoms?

- Pain on one side
- Pain on both sides
- Throbbing pain
- Constant pain
- Sensitive to light
- Sensitive to sound
- Worse with movement
- Nausea/vomiting
- Nasal congestion
- Feeling cold or warm
- Sensitive to smell/touch
- Neck pain
- Visual or other physical symptoms
- Other:_____

Potential triggers?

- Diet change
- Change in water/caffeine/alcohol intake
- Decreased sleep
- Medication change
- Increased stress
- Weather
- Amount of light
- Strong smells
- Loud sounds
- Hormone change
- Pressure on head
- Vitamin/mineral deficiency
- Change in exercise
- Travel
- Other:_____

Feelings afterward?

- Feel normal
- Depressed
- Very happy
- Fatigued
- Decreased concentration
- Other:_____

Additional details of headache:

Date:_____ Time:_____

How long did the headache last:_____

How severe is the pain? (Circle a number)

1   2   3   4   5   6   7   8   9   10

**Warning signs
(hours to days prior)?**
- Mood change
- Decreased concentration
- Visual disturbance
- Physical symptoms
- Fatigue
- Sensitivity to light, sounds, or smells
- Neck discomfort
- Difficult speaking/reading
- Nausea
- Change in bowel habits
- Food cravings/thirst
- Yawning
- Other:_____

Headache symptoms?
- Pain on one side
- Pain on both sides
- Throbbing pain
- Constant pain
- Sensitive to light
- Sensitive to sound
- Worse with movement
- Nausea/vomiting
- Nasal congestion
- Feeling cold or warm
- Sensitive to smell/touch
- Neck pain
- Visual or other physical symptoms
- Other:_____

Potential triggers?
- Diet change
- Change in water/caffeine/alcohol intake
- Decreased sleep
- Medication change
- Increased stress
- Weather
- Amount of light
- Strong smells
- Loud sounds
- Hormone change
- Pressure on head
- Vitamin/mineral deficiency
- Change in exercise
- Travel
- Other:_____

Feelings afterward?
- Feel normal
- Depressed
- Very happy
- Fatigued
- Decreased concentration
- Other:_____

Additional details of headache:

Date:_____ Time:_____

How long did the headache last:_____

How severe is the pain? (Circle a number)

1   2   3   4   5   6   7   8   9   10

Warning signs (hours to days prior)?

○ Mood change
○ Decreased concentration
○ Visual disturbance
○ Physical symptoms
○ Fatigue
○ Sensitivity to light, sounds, or smells
○ Neck discomfort
○ Difficult speaking/reading
○ Nausea
○ Change in bowel habits
○ Food cravings/thirst
○ Yawning
○ Other:_____

Headache symptoms?

○ Pain on one side
○ Pain on both sides
○ Throbbing pain
○ Constant pain
○ Sensitive to light
○ Sensitive to sound
○ Worse with movement
○ Nausea/vomiting
○ Nasal congestion
○ Feeling cold or warm
○ Sensitive to smell/touch
○ Neck pain
○ Visual or other physical symptoms
○ Other:_____

Potential triggers?

○ Diet change
○ Change in water/caffeine/alcohol intake
○ Decreased sleep
○ Medication change
○ Increased stress
○ Weather
○ Amount of light
○ Strong smells
○ Loud sounds
○ Hormone change
○ Pressure on head
○ Vitamin/mineral deficiency
○ Change in exercise
○ Travel
○ Other:_____

Feelings afterward?

○ Feel normal
○ Depressed
○ Very happy
○ Fatigued
○ Decreased concentration
○ Other:_____

Additional details of headache:

Date:_____ Time:_____

How long did the headache last:_____

How severe is the pain? (Circle a number)

1   2   3   4   5   6   7   8   9   10

Warning signs
(hours to days prior)?
Mood change
Decreased concentration
Visual disturbance
Physical symptoms
Fatigue
Sensitivity to light, sounds, or smells
Neck discomfort
Difficult speaking/reading
Nausea
Change in bowel habits
Food cravings/thirst
Yawning
Other:_____

Headache symptoms?
Pain on one side
Pain on both sides
Throbbing pain
Constant pain
Sensitive to light
Sensitive to sound
Worse with movement
Nausea/vomiting
Nasal congestion
Feeling cold or warm
Sensitive to smell/touch
Neck pain
Visual or other physical symptoms
Other:_____

Potential triggers?
Diet change
Change in water/caffeine/alcohol intake
Decreased sleep
Medication change
Increased stress
Weather
Amount of light
Strong smells
Loud sounds
Hormone change
Pressure on head
Vitamin/mineral deficiency
Change in exercise
Travel
Other:_____

Feelings afterward?
Feel normal
Depressed
Very happy
Fatigued
Decreased concentration
Other:_____

Additional details of headache:

Date:_____ Time:_____

How long did the headache last:_____

How severe is the pain? (Circle a number)

1 2 3 4 5 6 7 8 9 10

Warning signs (hours to days prior)?

- ○ Mood change
- ○ Decreased concentration
- ○ Visual disturbance
- ○ Physical symptoms
- ○ Fatigue
- ○ Sensitivity to light, sounds, or smells
- ○ Neck discomfort
- ○ Difficult speaking/reading
- ○ Nausea
- ○ Change in bowel habits
- ○ Food cravings/thirst
- ○ Yawning
- ○ Other:_____

Headache symptoms?

- ○ Pain on one side
- ○ Pain on both sides
- ○ Throbbing pain
- ○ Constant pain
- ○ Sensitive to light
- ○ Sensitive to sound
- ○ Worse with movement
- ○ Nausea/vomiting
- ○ Nasal congestion
- ○ Feeling cold or warm
- ○ Sensitive to smell/touch
- ○ Neck pain
- ○ Visual or other physical symptoms
- ○ Other:_____

Potential triggers?

- ○ Diet change
- ○ Change in water/caffeine/alcohol intake
- ○ Decreased sleep
- ○ Medication change
- ○ Increased stress
- ○ Weather
- ○ Amount of light
- ○ Strong smells
- ○ Loud sounds
- ○ Hormone change
- ○ Pressure on head
- ○ Vitamin/mineral deficiency
- ○ Change in exercise
- ○ Travel
- ○ Other:_____

Feelings afterward?

- ○ Feel normal
- ○ Depressed
- ○ Very happy
- ○ Fatigued
- ○ Decreased concentration
- ○ Other:_____

Additional details of headache:

Date:_____ Time:_____

How long did the headache last:_____

How severe is the pain? (Circle a number)

1 2 3 4 5 6 7 8 9 10

Warning signs (hours to days prior)?

- Mood change
- Decreased concentration
- Visual disturbance
- Physical symptoms
- Fatigue
- Sensitivity to light, sounds, or smells
- Neck discomfort
- Difficult speaking/reading
- Nausea
- Change in bowel habits
- Food cravings/thirst
- Yawning
- Other:_____

Headache symptoms?

- Pain on one side
- Pain on both sides
- Throbbing pain
- Constant pain
- Sensitive to light
- Sensitive to sound
- Worse with movement
- Nausea/vomiting
- Nasal congestion
- Feeling cold or warm
- Sensitive to smell/touch
- Neck pain
- Visual or other physical symptoms
- Other:_____

Potential triggers?

- Diet change
- Change in water/caffeine/alcohol intake
- Decreased sleep
- Medication change
- Increased stress
- Weather
- Amount of light
- Strong smells
- Loud sounds
- Hormone change
- Pressure on head
- Vitamin/mineral deficiency
- Change in exercise
- Travel
- Other:_____

Feelings afterward?

- Feel normal
- Depressed
- Very happy
- Fatigued
- Decreased concentration
- Other:_____

Additional details of headache:

Date:_____ Time:_____

How long did the headache last:_____

How severe is the pain? (Circle a number)

1   2   3   4   5   6   7   8   9   10

Warning signs (hours to days prior)?

- Mood change
- Decreased concentration
- Visual disturbance
- Physical symptoms
- Fatigue
- Sensitivity to light, sounds, or smells
- Neck discomfort
- Difficult speaking/reading
- Nausea
- Change in bowel habits
- Food cravings/thirst
- Yawning
- Other:_____

Headache symptoms?

- Pain on one side
- Pain on both sides
- Throbbing pain
- Constant pain
- Sensitive to light
- Sensitive to sound
- Worse with movement
- Nausea/vomiting
- Nasal congestion
- Feeling cold or warm
- Sensitive to smell/touch
- Neck pain
- Visual or other physical symptoms
- Other:_____

Potential triggers?

- Diet change
- Change in water/caffeine/alcohol intake
- Decreased sleep
- Medication change
- Increased stress
- Weather
- Amount of light
- Strong smells
- Loud sounds
- Hormone change
- Pressure on head
- Vitamin/mineral deficiency
- Change in exercise
- Travel
- Other:_____

Feelings afterward?

- Feel normal
- Depressed
- Very happy
- Fatigued
- Decreased concentration
- Other:_____

Additional details of headache:

Date:_____ Time:_____

How long did the headache last:_____

How severe is the pain? (Circle a number)

1   2   3   4   5   6   7   8   9   10

Warning signs (hours to days prior)?

- Mood change
- Decreased concentration
- Visual disturbance
- Physical symptoms
- Fatigue
- Sensitivity to light, sounds, or smells
- Neck discomfort
- Difficult speaking/reading
- Nausea
- Change in bowel habits
- Food cravings/thirst
- Yawning
- Other:_____

Headache symptoms?

- Pain on one side
- Pain on both sides
- Throbbing pain
- Constant pain
- Sensitive to light
- Sensitive to sound
- Worse with movement
- Nausea/vomiting
- Nasal congestion
- Feeling cold or warm
- Sensitive to smell/touch
- Neck pain
- Visual or other physical symptoms
- Other:_____

Potential triggers?

- Diet change
- Change in water/caffeine/alcohol intake
- Decreased sleep
- Medication change
- Increased stress
- Weather
- Amount of light
- Strong smells
- Loud sounds
- Hormone change
- Pressure on head
- Vitamin/mineral deficiency
- Change in exercise
- Travel
- Other:_____

Feelings afterward?

- Feel normal
- Depressed
- Very happy
- Fatigued
- Decreased concentration
- Other:_____

Additional details of headache:

Date:_____ Time:_____

How long did the headache last:_____

How severe is the pain? (Circle a number)

1 2 3 4 5 6 7 8 9 10

Warning signs (hours to days prior)?

- Mood change
- Decreased concentration
- Visual disturbance
- Physical symptoms
- Fatigue
- Sensitivity to light, sounds, or smells
- Neck discomfort
- Difficult speaking/reading
- Nausea
- Change in bowel habits
- Food cravings/thirst
- Yawning
- Other:_____

Headache symptoms?

- Pain on one side
- Pain on both sides
- Throbbing pain
- Constant pain
- Sensitive to light
- Sensitive to sound
- Worse with movement
- Nausea/vomiting
- Nasal congestion
- Feeling cold or warm
- Sensitive to smell/touch
- Neck pain
- Visual or other physical symptoms
- Other:_____

Potential triggers?

- Diet change
- Change in water/caffeine/alcohol intake
- Decreased sleep
- Medication change
- Increased stress
- Weather
- Amount of light
- Strong smells
- Loud sounds
- Hormone change
- Pressure on head
- Vitamin/mineral deficiency
- Change in exercise
- Travel
- Other:_____

Feelings afterward?

- Feel normal
- Depressed
- Very happy
- Fatigued
- Decreased concentration
- Other:_____

Additional details of headache:

Date:_____ Time:_____

How long did the headache last:_____

How severe is the pain? (Circle a number)

1 2 3 4 5 6 7 8 9 10

Warning signs (hours to days prior)?

- Mood change
- Decreased concentration
- Visual disturbance
- Physical symptoms
- Fatigue
- Sensitivity to light, sounds, or smells
- Neck discomfort
- Difficult speaking/reading
- Nausea
- Change in bowel habits
- Food cravings/thirst
- Yawning
- Other:_____

Headache symptoms?

- Pain on one side
- Pain on both sides
- Throbbing pain
- Constant pain
- Sensitive to light
- Sensitive to sound
- Worse with movement
- Nausea/vomiting
- Nasal congestion
- Feeling cold or warm
- Sensitive to smell/touch
- Neck pain
- Visual or other physical symptoms
- Other:_____

Potential triggers?

- Diet change
- Change in water/caffeine/alcohol intake
- Decreased sleep
- Medication change
- Increased stress
- Weather
- Amount of light
- Strong smells
- Loud sounds
- Hormone change
- Pressure on head
- Vitamin/mineral deficiency
- Change in exercise
- Travel
- Other:_____

Feelings afterward?

- Feel normal
- Depressed
- Very happy
- Fatigued
- Decreased concentration
- Other:_____

Additional details of headache:

Date:_____ Time:_____

How long did the headache last:_____

How severe is the pain? (Circle a number)

1 2 3 4 5 6 7 8 9 10

Warning signs (hours to days prior)?

- Mood change
- Decreased concentration
- Visual disturbance
- Physical symptoms
- Fatigue
- Sensitivity to light, sounds, or smells
- Neck discomfort
- Difficult speaking/reading
- Nausea
- Change in bowel habits
- Food cravings/thirst
- Yawning
- Other:_____

Headache symptoms?

- Pain on one side
- Pain on both sides
- Throbbing pain
- Constant pain
- Sensitive to light
- Sensitive to sound
- Worse with movement
- Nausea/vomiting
- Nasal congestion
- Feeling cold or warm
- Sensitive to smell/touch
- Neck pain
- Visual or other physical symptoms
- Other:_____

Potential triggers?

- Diet change
- Change in water/caffeine/alcohol intake
- Decreased sleep
- Medication change
- Increased stress
- Weather
- Amount of light
- Strong smells
- Loud sounds
- Hormone change
- Pressure on head
- Vitamin/mineral deficiency
- Change in exercise
- Travel
- Other:_____

Feelings afterward?

- Feel normal
- Depressed
- Very happy
- Fatigued
- Decreased concentration
- Other:_____

Additional details of headache:

Date:_____ Time:_____

How long did the headache last:_____

How severe is the pain? (Circle a number)

1 2 3 4 5 6 7 8 9 10

Warning signs (hours to days prior)?

- ○ Mood change
- ○ Decreased concentration
- ○ Visual disturbance
- ○ Physical symptoms
- ○ Fatigue
- ○ Sensitivity to light, sounds, or smells
- ○ Neck discomfort
- ○ Difficult speaking/reading
- ○ Nausea
- ○ Change in bowel habits
- ○ Food cravings/thirst
- ○ Yawning
- ○ Other:_____

Headache symptoms?

- ○ Pain on one side
- ○ Pain on both sides
- ○ Throbbing pain
- ○ Constant pain
- ○ Sensitive to light
- ○ Sensitive to sound
- ○ Worse with movement
- ○ Nausea/vomiting
- ○ Nasal congestion
- ○ Feeling cold or warm
- ○ Sensitive to smell/touch
- ○ Neck pain
- ○ Visual or other physical symptoms
- ○ Other:_____

Potential triggers?

- ○ Diet change
- ○ Change in water/caffeine/alcohol intake
- ○ Decreased sleep
- ○ Medication change
- ○ Increased stress
- ○ Weather
- ○ Amount of light
- ○ Strong smells
- ○ Loud sounds
- ○ Hormone change
- ○ Pressure on head
- ○ Vitamin/mineral deficiency
- ○ Change in exercise
- ○ Travel
- ○ Other:_____

Feelings afterward?

- ○ Feel normal
- ○ Depressed
- ○ Very happy
- ○ Fatigued
- ○ Decreased concentration
- ○ Other:_____

Additional details of headache:

Date:_____ Time:_____

How long did the headache last:_____

How severe is the pain? (Circle a number)

1 2 3 4 5 6 7 8 9 10

Warning signs (hours to days prior)?
- Mood change
- Decreased concentration
- Visual disturbance
- Physical symptoms
- Fatigue
- Sensitivity to light, sounds, or smells
- Neck discomfort
- Difficult speaking/reading
- Nausea
- Change in bowel habits
- Food cravings/thirst
- Yawning
- Other:_____

Headache symptoms?
- Pain on one side
- Pain on both sides
- Throbbing pain
- Constant pain
- Sensitive to light
- Sensitive to sound
- Worse with movement
- Nausea/vomiting
- Nasal congestion
- Feeling cold or warm
- Sensitive to smell/touch
- Neck pain
- Visual or other physical symptoms
- Other:_____

Potential triggers?
- Diet change
- Change in water/caffeine/alcohol intake
- Decreased sleep
- Medication change
- Increased stress
- Weather
- Amount of light
- Strong smells
- Loud sounds
- Hormone change
- Pressure on head
- Vitamin/mineral deficiency
- Change in exercise
- Travel
- Other:_____

Feelings afterward?
- Feel normal
- Depressed
- Very happy
- Fatigued
- Decreased concentration
- Other:_____

Additional details of headache:

Date:_____ Time:_____

How long did the headache last:_____

How severe is the pain? (Circle a number)

1 2 3 4 5 6 7 8 9 10

Warning signs (hours to days prior)?

- Mood change
- Decreased concentration
- Visual disturbance
- Physical symptoms
- Fatigue
- Sensitivity to light, sounds, or smells
- Neck discomfort
- Difficult speaking/reading
- Nausea
- Change in bowel habits
- Food cravings/thirst
- Yawning
- Other:_____

Headache symptoms?

- Pain on one side
- Pain on both sides
- Throbbing pain
- Constant pain
- Sensitive to light
- Sensitive to sound
- Worse with movement
- Nausea/vomiting
- Nasal congestion
- Feeling cold or warm
- Sensitive to smell/touch
- Neck pain
- Visual or other physical symptoms
- Other:_____

Potential triggers?

- Diet change
- Change in water/caffeine/alcohol intake
- Decreased sleep
- Medication change
- Increased stress
- Weather
- Amount of light
- Strong smells
- Loud sounds
- Hormone change
- Pressure on head
- Vitamin/mineral deficiency
- Change in exercise
- Travel
- Other:_____

Feelings afterward?

- Feel normal
- Depressed
- Very happy
- Fatigued
- Decreased concentration
- Other:_____

Additional details of headache:

Date:_____ Time:_____

How long did the headache last:_____

How severe is the pain? (Circle a number)

1   2   3   4   5   6   7   8   9   10

Warning signs (hours to days prior)?

- ○ Mood change
- ○ Decreased concentration
- ○ Visual disturbance
- ○ Physical symptoms
- ○ Fatigue
- ○ Sensitivity to light, sounds, or smells
- ○ Neck discomfort
- ○ Difficult speaking/reading
- ○ Nausea
- ○ Change in bowel habits
- ○ Food cravings/thirst
- ○ Yawning
- ○ Other:_____

Headache symptoms?

- ○ Pain on one side
- ○ Pain on both sides
- ○ Throbbing pain
- ○ Constant pain
- ○ Sensitive to light
- ○ Sensitive to sound
- ○ Worse with movement
- ○ Nausea/vomiting
- ○ Nasal congestion
- ○ Feeling cold or warm
- ○ Sensitive to smell/touch
- ○ Neck pain
- ○ Visual or other physical symptoms
- ○ Other:_____

Potential triggers?

- ○ Diet change
- ○ Change in water/caffeine/alcohol intake
- ○ Decreased sleep
- ○ Medication change
- ○ Increased stress
- ○ Weather
- ○ Amount of light
- ○ Strong smells
- ○ Loud sounds
- ○ Hormone change
- ○ Pressure on head
- ○ Vitamin/mineral deficiency
- ○ Change in exercise
- ○ Travel
- ○ Other:_____

Feelings afterward?

- ○ Feel normal
- ○ Depressed
- ○ Very happy
- ○ Fatigued
- ○ Decreased concentration
- ○ Other:_____

Additional details of headache:

Date:_____ Time:_____

How long did the headache last:_____

How severe is the pain? (Circle a number)

1 2 3 4 5 6 7 8 9 10

Warning signs (hours to days prior)?

- Mood change
- Decreased concentration
- Visual disturbance
- Physical symptoms
- Fatigue
- Sensitivity to light, sounds, or smells
- Neck discomfort
- Difficult speaking/reading
- Nausea
- Change in bowel habits
- Food cravings/thirst
- Yawning
- Other:_____

Headache symptoms?

- Pain on one side
- Pain on both sides
- Throbbing pain
- Constant pain
- Sensitive to light
- Sensitive to sound
- Worse with movement
- Nausea/vomiting
- Nasal congestion
- Feeling cold or warm
- Sensitive to smell/touch
- Neck pain
- Visual or other physical symptoms
- Other:_____

Potential triggers?

- Diet change
- Change in water/caffeine/alcohol intake
- Decreased sleep
- Medication change
- Increased stress
- Weather
- Amount of light
- Strong smells
- Loud sounds
- Hormone change
- Pressure on head
- Vitamin/mineral deficiency
- Change in exercise
- Travel
- Other:_____

Feelings afterward?

- Feel normal
- Depressed
- Very happy
- Fatigued
- Decreased concentration
- Other:_____

Additional details of headache:

Date:_____ Time:_____

How long did the headache last:_____

How severe is the pain? (Circle a number)

1 2 3 4 5 6 7 8 9 10

Warning signs (hours to days prior)?

- Mood change
- Decreased concentration
- Visual disturbance
- Physical symptoms
- Fatigue
- Sensitivity to light, sounds, or smells
- Neck discomfort
- Difficult speaking/reading
- Nausea
- Change in bowel habits
- Food cravings/thirst
- Yawning
- Other:_____

Headache symptoms?

- Pain on one side
- Pain on both sides
- Throbbing pain
- Constant pain
- Sensitive to light
- Sensitive to sound
- Worse with movement
- Nausea/vomiting
- Nasal congestion
- Feeling cold or warm
- Sensitive to smell/touch
- Neck pain
- Visual or other physical symptoms
- Other:_____

Potential triggers?

- Diet change
- Change in water/caffeine/alcohol intake
- Decreased sleep
- Medication change
- Increased stress
- Weather
- Amount of light
- Strong smells
- Loud sounds
- Hormone change
- Pressure on head
- Vitamin/mineral deficiency
- Change in exercise
- Travel
- Other:_____

Feelings afterward?

- Feel normal
- Depressed
- Very happy
- Fatigued
- Decreased concentration
- Other:_____

Additional details of headache:

Date:_____ Time:_____

How long did the headache last:_____

How severe is the pain? (Circle a number)

1 2 3 4 5 6 7 8 9 10

Warning signs (hours to days prior)?

- Mood change
- Decreased concentration
- Visual disturbance
- Physical symptoms
- Fatigue
- Sensitivity to light, sounds, or smells
- Neck discomfort
- Difficult speaking/reading
- Nausea
- Change in bowel habits
- Food cravings/thirst
- Yawning
- Other:_____

Headache symptoms?

- Pain on one side
- Pain on both sides
- Throbbing pain
- Constant pain
- Sensitive to light
- Sensitive to sound
- Worse with movement
- Nausea/vomiting
- Nasal congestion
- Feeling cold or warm
- Sensitive to smell/touch
- Neck pain
- Visual or other physical symptoms
- Other:_____

Potential triggers?

- Diet change
- Change in water/caffeine/alcohol intake
- Decreased sleep
- Medication change
- Increased stress
- Weather
- Amount of light
- Strong smells
- Loud sounds
- Hormone change
- Pressure on head
- Vitamin/mineral deficiency
- Change in exercise
- Travel
- Other:_____

Feelings afterward?

- Feel normal
- Depressed
- Very happy
- Fatigued
- Decreased concentration
- Other:_____

Additional details of headache:

Date:_____ Time:_____

How long did the headache last:_____

How severe is the pain? (Circle a number)

1 2 3 4 5 6 7 8 9 10

Warning signs (hours to days prior)?

- Mood change
- Decreased concentration
- Visual disturbance
- Physical symptoms
- Fatigue
- Sensitivity to light, sounds, or smells
- Neck discomfort
- Difficult speaking/reading
- Nausea
- Change in bowel habits
- Food cravings/thirst
- Yawning
- Other:_____

Headache symptoms?

- Pain on one side
- Pain on both sides
- Throbbing pain
- Constant pain
- Sensitive to light
- Sensitive to sound
- Worse with movement
- Nausea/vomiting
- Nasal congestion
- Feeling cold or warm
- Sensitive to smell/touch
- Neck pain
- Visual or other physical symptoms
- Other:_____

Potential triggers?

- Diet change
- Change in water/caffeine/alcohol intake
- Decreased sleep
- Medication change
- Increased stress
- Weather
- Amount of light
- Strong smells
- Loud sounds
- Hormone change
- Pressure on head
- Vitamin/mineral deficiency
- Change in exercise
- Travel
- Other:_____

Feelings afterward?

- Feel normal
- Depressed
- Very happy
- Fatigued
- Decreased concentration
- Other:_____

Additional details of headache:

Date:_____ Time:_____

How long did the headache last:_____

How severe is the pain? (Circle a number)

1 2 3 4 5 6 7 8 9 10

Warning signs (hours to days prior)?

- Mood change
- Decreased concentration
- Visual disturbance
- Physical symptoms
- Fatigue
- Sensitivity to light, sounds, or smells
- Neck discomfort
- Difficult speaking/reading
- Nausea
- Change in bowel habits
- Food cravings/thirst
- Yawning
- Other:_____

Headache symptoms?

- Pain on one side
- Pain on both sides
- Throbbing pain
- Constant pain
- Sensitive to light
- Sensitive to sound
- Worse with movement
- Nausea/vomiting
- Nasal congestion
- Feeling cold or warm
- Sensitive to smell/touch
- Neck pain
- Visual or other physical symptoms
- Other:_____

Potential triggers?

- Diet change
- Change in water/caffeine/alcohol intake
- Decreased sleep
- Medication change
- Increased stress
- Weather
- Amount of light
- Strong smells
- Loud sounds
- Hormone change
- Pressure on head
- Vitamin/mineral deficiency
- Change in exercise
- Travel
- Other:_____

Feelings afterward?

- Feel normal
- Depressed
- Very happy
- Fatigued
- Decreased concentration
- Other:_____

Additional details of headache:

Date:_____ Time:_____

How long did the headache last:_____

How severe is the pain? (Circle a number)

1   2   3   4   5   6   7   8   9   10

Warning signs (hours to days prior)?

- Mood change
- Decreased concentration
- Visual disturbance
- Physical symptoms
- Fatigue
- Sensitivity to light, sounds, or smells
- Neck discomfort
- Difficult speaking/reading
- Nausea
- Change in bowel habits
- Food cravings/thirst
- Yawning
- Other:_____

Headache symptoms?

- Pain on one side
- Pain on both sides
- Throbbing pain
- Constant pain
- Sensitive to light
- Sensitive to sound
- Worse with movement
- Nausea/vomiting
- Nasal congestion
- Feeling cold or warm
- Sensitive to smell/touch
- Neck pain
- Visual or other physical symptoms
- Other:_____

Potential triggers?

- Diet change
- Change in water/caffeine/alcohol intake
- Decreased sleep
- Medication change
- Increased stress
- Weather
- Amount of light
- Strong smells
- Loud sounds
- Hormone change
- Pressure on head
- Vitamin/mineral deficiency
- Change in exercise
- Travel
- Other:_____

Feelings afterward?

- Feel normal
- Depressed
- Very happy
- Fatigued
- Decreased concentration
- Other:_____

Additional details of headache:

Date:_____ Time:_____

How long did the headache last:_____

How severe is the pain? (Circle a number)

1 2 3 4 5 6 7 8 9 10

Warning signs (hours to days prior)?

- Mood change
- Decreased concentration
- Visual disturbance
- Physical symptoms
- Fatigue
- Sensitivity to light, sounds, or smells
- Neck discomfort
- Difficult speaking/reading
- Nausea
- Change in bowel habits
- Food cravings/thirst
- Yawning
- Other:_____

Headache symptoms?

- Pain on one side
- Pain on both sides
- Throbbing pain
- Constant pain
- Sensitive to light
- Sensitive to sound
- Worse with movement
- Nausea/vomiting
- Nasal congestion
- Feeling cold or warm
- Sensitive to smell/touch
- Neck pain
- Visual or other physical symptoms
- Other:_____

Potential triggers?

- Diet change
- Change in water/caffeine/alcohol intake
- Decreased sleep
- Medication change
- Increased stress
- Weather
- Amount of light
- Strong smells
- Loud sounds
- Hormone change
- Pressure on head
- Vitamin/mineral deficiency
- Change in exercise
- Travel
- Other:_____

Feelings afterward?

- Feel normal
- Depressed
- Very happy
- Fatigued
- Decreased concentration
- Other:_____

Additional details of headache:

Date:_____ Time:_____

How long did the headache last:_____

How severe is the pain? (Circle a number)

1 2 3 4 5 6 7 8 9 10

Warning signs (hours to days prior)?

- ○ Mood change
- ○ Decreased concentration
- ○ Visual disturbance
- ○ Physical symptoms
- ○ Fatigue
- ○ Sensitivity to light, sounds, or smells
- ○ Neck discomfort
- ○ Difficult speaking/reading
- ○ Nausea
- ○ Change in bowel habits
- ○ Food cravings/thirst
- ○ Yawning
- ○ Other:_____

Headache symptoms?

- ○ Pain on one side
- ○ Pain on both sides
- ○ Throbbing pain
- ○ Constant pain
- ○ Sensitive to light
- ○ Sensitive to sound
- ○ Worse with movement
- ○ Nausea/vomiting
- ○ Nasal congestion
- ○ Feeling cold or warm
- ○ Sensitive to smell/touch
- ○ Neck pain
- ○ Visual or other physical symptoms
- ○ Other:_____

Potential triggers?

- ○ Diet change
- ○ Change in water/caffeine/alcohol intake
- ○ Decreased sleep
- ○ Medication change
- ○ Increased stress
- ○ Weather
- ○ Amount of light
- ○ Strong smells
- ○ Loud sounds
- ○ Hormone change
- ○ Pressure on head
- ○ Vitamin/mineral deficiency
- ○ Change in exercise
- ○ Travel
- ○ Other:_____

Feelings afterward?

- ○ Feel normal
- ○ Depressed
- ○ Very happy
- ○ Fatigued
- ○ Decreased concentration
- ○ Other:_____

Additional details of headache:

Date:_____ Time:_____

How long did the headache last:_____

How severe is the pain? (Circle a number)

1   2   3   4   5   6   7   8   9   10

Warning signs (hours to days prior)?

- Mood change
- Decreased concentration
- Visual disturbance
- Physical symptoms
- Fatigue
- Sensitivity to light, sounds, or smells
- Neck discomfort
- Difficult speaking/reading
- Nausea
- Change in bowel habits
- Food cravings/thirst
- Yawning
- Other:_____

Headache symptoms?

- Pain on one side
- Pain on both sides
- Throbbing pain
- Constant pain
- Sensitive to light
- Sensitive to sound
- Worse with movement
- Nausea/vomiting
- Nasal congestion
- Feeling cold or warm
- Sensitive to smell/touch
- Neck pain
- Visual or other physical symptoms
- Other:_____

Potential triggers?

- Diet change
- Change in water/caffeine/alcohol intake
- Decreased sleep
- Medication change
- Increased stress
- Weather
- Amount of light
- Strong smells
- Loud sounds
- Hormone change
- Pressure on head
- Vitamin/mineral deficiency
- Change in exercise
- Travel
- Other:_____

Feelings afterward?

- Feel normal
- Depressed
- Very happy
- Fatigued
- Decreased concentration
- Other:_____

Additional details of headache:

Date:_____ Time:_____

How long did the headache last:_____

How severe is the pain? (Circle a number)

1   2   3   4   5   6   7   8   9   10

Warning signs (hours to days prior)?

- ○ Mood change
- ○ Decreased concentration
- ○ Visual disturbance
- ○ Physical symptoms
- ○ Fatigue
- ○ Sensitivity to light, sounds, or smells
- ○ Neck discomfort
- ○ Difficult speaking/reading
- ○ Nausea
- ○ Change in bowel habits
- ○ Food cravings/thirst
- ○ Yawning
- ○ Other:_____

Headache symptoms?

- ○ Pain on one side
- ○ Pain on both sides
- ○ Throbbing pain
- ○ Constant pain
- ○ Sensitive to light
- ○ Sensitive to sound
- ○ Worse with movement
- ○ Nausea/vomiting
- ○ Nasal congestion
- ○ Feeling cold or warm
- ○ Sensitive to smell/touch
- ○ Neck pain
- ○ Visual or other physical symptoms
- ○ Other:_____

Potential triggers?

- ○ Diet change
- ○ Change in water/caffeine/alcohol intake
- ○ Decreased sleep
- ○ Medication change
- ○ Increased stress
- ○ Weather
- ○ Amount of light
- ○ Strong smells
- ○ Loud sounds
- ○ Hormone change
- ○ Pressure on head
- ○ Vitamin/mineral deficiency
- ○ Change in exercise
- ○ Travel
- ○ Other:_____

Feelings afterward?

- ○ Feel normal
- ○ Depressed
- ○ Very happy
- ○ Fatigued
- ○ Decreased concentration
- ○ Other:_____

Additional details of headache:

Date:_____ Time:_____

How long did the headache last:_____

How severe is the pain? (Circle a number)

1 2 3 4 5 6 7 8 9 10

Warning signs (hours to days prior)?

- Mood change
- Decreased concentration
- Visual disturbance
- Physical symptoms
- Fatigue
- Sensitivity to light, sounds, or smells
- Neck discomfort
- Difficult speaking/reading
- Nausea
- Change in bowel habits
- Food cravings/thirst
- Yawning
- Other:_____

Headache symptoms?

- Pain on one side
- Pain on both sides
- Throbbing pain
- Constant pain
- Sensitive to light
- Sensitive to sound
- Worse with movement
- Nausea/vomiting
- Nasal congestion
- Feeling cold or warm
- Sensitive to smell/touch
- Neck pain
- Visual or other physical symptoms
- Other:_____

Potential triggers?

- Diet change
- Change in water/caffeine/alcohol intake
- Decreased sleep
- Medication change
- Increased stress
- Weather
- Amount of light
- Strong smells
- Loud sounds
- Hormone change
- Pressure on head
- Vitamin/mineral deficiency
- Change in exercise
- Travel
- Other:_____

Feelings afterward?

- Feel normal
- Depressed
- Very happy
- Fatigued
- Decreased concentration
- Other:_____

Additional details of headache:

Date:_____ Time:_____

How long did the headache last:_____

How severe is the pain? (Circle a number)

1 2 3 4 5 6 7 8 9 10

Warning signs (hours to days prior)?

- ○ Mood change
- ○ Decreased concentration
- ○ Visual disturbance
- ○ Physical symptoms
- ○ Fatigue
- ○ Sensitivity to light, sounds, or smells
- ○ Neck discomfort
- ○ Difficult speaking/reading
- ○ Nausea
- ○ Change in bowel habits
- ○ Food cravings/thirst
- ○ Yawning
- ○ Other:_____

Headache symptoms?

- ○ Pain on one side
- ○ Pain on both sides
- ○ Throbbing pain
- ○ Constant pain
- ○ Sensitive to light
- ○ Sensitive to sound
- ○ Worse with movement
- ○ Nausea/vomiting
- ○ Nasal congestion
- ○ Feeling cold or warm
- ○ Sensitive to smell/touch
- ○ Neck pain
- ○ Visual or other physical symptoms
- ○ Other:_____

Potential triggers?

- ○ Diet change
- ○ Change in water/caffeine/alcohol intake
- ○ Decreased sleep
- ○ Medication change
- ○ Increased stress
- ○ Weather
- ○ Amount of light
- ○ Strong smells
- ○ Loud sounds
- ○ Hormone change
- ○ Pressure on head
- ○ Vitamin/mineral deficiency
- ○ Change in exercise
- ○ Travel
- ○ Other:_____

Feelings afterward?

- ○ Feel normal
- ○ Depressed
- ○ Very happy
- ○ Fatigued
- ○ Decreased concentration
- ○ Other:_____

Additional details of headache:

Date:_____ Time:_____

How long did the headache last:_____

How severe is the pain? (Circle a number)

1 2 3 4 5 6 7 8 9 10

Warning signs (hours to days prior)?

- Mood change
- Decreased concentration
- Visual disturbance
- Physical symptoms
- Fatigue
- Sensitivity to light, sounds, or smells
- Neck discomfort
- Difficult speaking/reading
- Nausea
- Change in bowel habits
- Food cravings/thirst
- Yawning
- Other:_____

Headache symptoms?

- Pain on one side
- Pain on both sides
- Throbbing pain
- Constant pain
- Sensitive to light
- Sensitive to sound
- Worse with movement
- Nausea/vomiting
- Nasal congestion
- Feeling cold or warm
- Sensitive to smell/touch
- Neck pain
- Visual or other physical symptoms
- Other:_____

Potential triggers?

- Diet change
- Change in water/caffeine/alcohol intake
- Decreased sleep
- Medication change
- Increased stress
- Weather
- Amount of light
- Strong smells
- Loud sounds
- Hormone change
- Pressure on head
- Vitamin/mineral deficiency
- Change in exercise
- Travel
- Other:_____

Feelings afterward?

- Feel normal
- Depressed
- Very happy
- Fatigued
- Decreased concentration
- Other:_____

Additional details of headache:

Date:_____ Time:_____

How long did the headache last:_____

How severe is the pain? (Circle a number)

1   2   3   4   5   6   7   8   9   10

Warning signs (hours to days prior)?
- ○ Mood change
- ○ Decreased concentration
- ○ Visual disturbance
- ○ Physical symptoms
- ○ Fatigue
- ○ Sensitivity to light, sounds, or smells
- ○ Neck discomfort
- ○ Difficult speaking/reading
- ○ Nausea
- ○ Change in bowel habits
- ○ Food cravings/thirst
- ○ Yawning
- ○ Other:_____

Headache symptoms?
- ○ Pain on one side
- ○ Pain on both sides
- ○ Throbbing pain
- ○ Constant pain
- ○ Sensitive to light
- ○ Sensitive to sound
- ○ Worse with movement
- ○ Nausea/vomiting
- ○ Nasal congestion
- ○ Feeling cold or warm
- ○ Sensitive to smell/touch
- ○ Neck pain
- ○ Visual or other physical symptoms
- ○ Other:_____

Potential triggers?
- ○ Diet change
- ○ Change in water/caffeine/alcohol intake
- ○ Decreased sleep
- ○ Medication change
- ○ Increased stress
- ○ Weather
- ○ Amount of light
- ○ Strong smells
- ○ Loud sounds
- ○ Hormone change
- ○ Pressure on head
- ○ Vitamin/mineral deficiency
- ○ Change in exercise
- ○ Travel
- ○ Other:_____

Feelings afterward?
- ○ Feel normal
- ○ Depressed
- ○ Very happy
- ○ Fatigued
- ○ Decreased concentration
- ○ Other:_____

Additional details of headache:

Date:_____ Time:_____

How long did the headache last:_____

How severe is the pain? (Circle a number)

1   2   3   4   5   6   7   8   9   10

Warning signs (hours to days prior)?

- Mood change
- Decreased concentration
- Visual disturbance
- Physical symptoms
- Fatigue
- Sensitivity to light, sounds, or smells
- Neck discomfort
- Difficult speaking/reading
- Nausea
- Change in bowel habits
- Food cravings/thirst
- Yawning
- Other:_____

Potential triggers?

- Diet change
- Change in water/caffeine/alcohol intake
- Decreased sleep
- Medication change
- Increased stress
- Weather
- Amount of light
- Strong smells
- Loud sounds
- Hormone change
- Pressure on head
- Vitamin/mineral deficiency
- Change in exercise
- Travel
- Other:_____

Headache symptoms?

- Pain on one side
- Pain on both sides
- Throbbing pain
- Constant pain
- Sensitive to light
- Sensitive to sound
- Worse with movement
- Nausea/vomiting
- Nasal congestion
- Feeling cold or warm
- Sensitive to smell/touch
- Neck pain
- Visual or other physical symptoms
- Other:_____

Feelings afterward?

- Feel normal
- Depressed
- Very happy
- Fatigued
- Decreased concentration
- Other:_____

Additional details of headache:

Date:_____ Time:_____

How long did the headache last:_____

How severe is the pain? (Circle a number)

1   2   3   4   5   6   7   8   9   10

Warning signs (hours to days prior)?

- Mood change
- Decreased concentration
- Visual disturbance
- Physical symptoms
- Fatigue
- Sensitivity to light, sounds, or smells
- Neck discomfort
- Difficult speaking/reading
- Nausea
- Change in bowel habits
- Food cravings/thirst
- Yawning
- Other:_____

Headache symptoms?

- Pain on one side
- Pain on both sides
- Throbbing pain
- Constant pain
- Sensitive to light
- Sensitive to sound
- Worse with movement
- Nausea/vomiting
- Nasal congestion
- Feeling cold or warm
- Sensitive to smell/touch
- Neck pain
- Visual or other physical symptoms
- Other:_____

Potential triggers?

- Diet change
- Change in water/caffeine/alcohol intake
- Decreased sleep
- Medication change
- Increased stress
- Weather
- Amount of light
- Strong smells
- Loud sounds
- Hormone change
- Pressure on head
- Vitamin/mineral deficiency
- Change in exercise
- Travel
- Other:_____

Feelings afterward?

- Feel normal
- Depressed
- Very happy
- Fatigued
- Decreased concentration
- Other:_____

Additional details of headache:

Date:_____ Time:_____

How long did the headache last:_____

How severe is the pain? (Circle a number)

1 2 3 4 5 6 7 8 9 10

Warning signs (hours to days prior)?

- Mood change
- Decreased concentration
- Visual disturbance
- Physical symptoms
- Fatigue
- Sensitivity to light, sounds, or smells
- Neck discomfort
- Difficult speaking/reading
- Nausea
- Change in bowel habits
- Food cravings/thirst
- Yawning
- Other:_____

Headache symptoms?

- Pain on one side
- Pain on both sides
- Throbbing pain
- Constant pain
- Sensitive to light
- Sensitive to sound
- Worse with movement
- Nausea/vomiting
- Nasal congestion
- Feeling cold or warm
- Sensitive to smell/touch
- Neck pain
- Visual or other physical symptoms
- Other:_____

Potential triggers?

- Diet change
- Change in water/caffeine/alcohol intake
- Decreased sleep
- Medication change
- Increased stress
- Weather
- Amount of light
- Strong smells
- Loud sounds
- Hormone change
- Pressure on head
- Vitamin/mineral deficiency
- Change in exercise
- Travel
- Other:_____

Feelings afterward?

- Feel normal
- Depressed
- Very happy
- Fatigued
- Decreased concentration
- Other:_____

Additional details of headache:

Date:_____ Time:_____

How long did the headache last:_____

How severe is the pain? (Circle a number)

1   2   3   4   5   6   7   8   9   10

Warning signs (hours to days prior)?

- ○ Mood change
- ○ Decreased concentration
- ○ Visual disturbance
- ○ Physical symptoms
- ○ Fatigue
- ○ Sensitivity to light, sounds, or smells
- ○ Neck discomfort
- ○ Difficult speaking/reading
- ○ Nausea
- ○ Change in bowel habits
- ○ Food cravings/thirst
- ○ Yawning
- ○ Other:_____

Headache symptoms?

- ○ Pain on one side
- ○ Pain on both sides
- ○ Throbbing pain
- ○ Constant pain
- ○ Sensitive to light
- ○ Sensitive to sound
- ○ Worse with movement
- ○ Nausea/vomiting
- ○ Nasal congestion
- ○ Feeling cold or warm
- ○ Sensitive to smell/touch
- ○ Neck pain
- ○ Visual or other physical symptoms
- ○ Other:_____

Potential triggers?

- ○ Diet change
- ○ Change in water/caffeine/alcohol intake
- ○ Decreased sleep
- ○ Medication change
- ○ Increased stress
- ○ Weather
- ○ Amount of light
- ○ Strong smells
- ○ Loud sounds
- ○ Hormone change
- ○ Pressure on head
- ○ Vitamin/mineral deficiency
- ○ Change in exercise
- ○ Travel
- ○ Other:_____

Feelings afterward?

- ○ Feel normal
- ○ Depressed
- ○ Very happy
- ○ Fatigued
- ○ Decreased concentration
- ○ Other:_____

Additional details of headache:

Date:_____ Time:_____

How long did the headache last:_____

How severe is the pain? (Circle a number)

1 2 3 4 5 6 7 8 9 10

Warning signs (hours to days prior)?

- Mood change
- Decreased concentration
- Visual disturbance
- Physical symptoms
- Fatigue
- Sensitivity to light, sounds, or smells
- Neck discomfort
- Difficult speaking/reading
- Nausea
- Change in bowel habits
- Food cravings/thirst
- Yawning
- Other:_____

Headache symptoms?

- Pain on one side
- Pain on both sides
- Throbbing pain
- Constant pain
- Sensitive to light
- Sensitive to sound
- Worse with movement
- Nausea/vomiting
- Nasal congestion
- Feeling cold or warm
- Sensitive to smell/touch
- Neck pain
- Visual or other physical symptoms
- Other:_____

Potential triggers?

- Diet change
- Change in water/caffeine/alcohol intake
- Decreased sleep
- Medication change
- Increased stress
- Weather
- Amount of light
- Strong smells
- Loud sounds
- Hormone change
- Pressure on head
- Vitamin/mineral deficiency
- Change in exercise
- Travel
- Other:_____

Feelings afterward?

- Feel normal
- Depressed
- Very happy
- Fatigued
- Decreased concentration
- Other:_____

Additional details of headache:

Date:_____ Time:_____

How long did the headache last:_____

How severe is the pain? (Circle a number)

1   2   3   4   5   6   7   8   9   10

Warning signs (hours to days prior)?

- ○ Mood change
- ○ Decreased concentration
- ○ Visual disturbance
- ○ Physical symptoms
- ○ Fatigue
- ○ Sensitivity to light, sounds, or smells
- ○ Neck discomfort
- ○ Difficult speaking/reading
- ○ Nausea
- ○ Change in bowel habits
- ○ Food cravings/thirst
- ○ Yawning
- ○ Other:_____

Headache symptoms?

- ○ Pain on one side
- ○ Pain on both sides
- ○ Throbbing pain
- ○ Constant pain
- ○ Sensitive to light
- ○ Sensitive to sound
- ○ Worse with movement
- ○ Nausea/vomiting
- ○ Nasal congestion
- ○ Feeling cold or warm
- ○ Sensitive to smell/touch
- ○ Neck pain
- ○ Visual or other physical symptoms
- ○ Other:_____

Potential triggers?

- ○ Diet change
- ○ Change in water/caffeine/alcohol intake
- ○ Decreased sleep
- ○ Medication change
- ○ Increased stress
- ○ Weather
- ○ Amount of light
- ○ Strong smells
- ○ Loud sounds
- ○ Hormone change
- ○ Pressure on head
- ○ Vitamin/mineral deficiency
- ○ Change in exercise
- ○ Travel
- ○ Other:_____

Feelings afterward?

- ○ Feel normal
- ○ Depressed
- ○ Very happy
- ○ Fatigued
- ○ Decreased concentration
- ○ Other:_____

Additional details of headache:

Date:_____ Time:_____

How long did the headache last:_____

How severe is the pain? (Circle a number)

1   2   3   4   5   6   7   8   9   10

Warning signs (hours to days prior)?

- Mood change
- Decreased concentration
- Visual disturbance
- Physical symptoms
- Fatigue
- Sensitivity to light, sounds, or smells
- Neck discomfort
- Difficult speaking/reading
- Nausea
- Change in bowel habits
- Food cravings/thirst
- Yawning
- Other:_____

Headache symptoms?

- Pain on one side
- Pain on both sides
- Throbbing pain
- Constant pain
- Sensitive to light
- Sensitive to sound
- Worse with movement
- Nausea/vomiting
- Nasal congestion
- Feeling cold or warm
- Sensitive to smell/touch
- Neck pain
- Visual or other physical symptoms
- Other:_____

Potential triggers?

- Diet change
- Change in water/caffeine/alcohol intake
- Decreased sleep
- Medication change
- Increased stress
- Weather
- Amount of light
- Strong smells
- Loud sounds
- Hormone change
- Pressure on head
- Vitamin/mineral deficiency
- Change in exercise
- Travel
- Other:_____

Feelings afterward?

- Feel normal
- Depressed
- Very happy
- Fatigued
- Decreased concentration
- Other:_____

Additional details of headache:

Date:_____ Time:_____

How long did the headache last:_____

How severe is the pain? (Circle a number)

1 2 3 4 5 6 7 8 9 10

Warning signs (hours to days prior)?

- ○ Mood change
- ○ Decreased concentration
- ○ Visual disturbance
- ○ Physical symptoms
- ○ Fatigue
- ○ Sensitivity to light, sounds, or smells
- ○ Neck discomfort
- ○ Difficult speaking/reading
- ○ Nausea
- ○ Change in bowel habits
- ○ Food cravings/thirst
- ○ Yawning
- ○ Other:_____

Headache symptoms?

- ○ Pain on one side
- ○ Pain on both sides
- ○ Throbbing pain
- ○ Constant pain
- ○ Sensitive to light
- ○ Sensitive to sound
- ○ Worse with movement
- ○ Nausea/vomiting
- ○ Nasal congestion
- ○ Feeling cold or warm
- ○ Sensitive to smell/touch
- ○ Neck pain
- ○ Visual or other physical symptoms
- ○ Other:_____

Potential triggers?

- ○ Diet change
- ○ Change in water/caffeine/alcohol intake
- ○ Decreased sleep
- ○ Medication change
- ○ Increased stress
- ○ Weather
- ○ Amount of light
- ○ Strong smells
- ○ Loud sounds
- ○ Hormone change
- ○ Pressure on head
- ○ Vitamin/mineral deficiency
- ○ Change in exercise
- ○ Travel
- ○ Other:_____

Feelings afterward?

- ○ Feel normal
- ○ Depressed
- ○ Very happy
- ○ Fatigued
- ○ Decreased concentration
- ○ Other:_____

Additional details of headache:

Date:_____ Time:_____

How long did the headache last:_____

How severe is the pain? (Circle a number)

1   2   3   4   5   6   7   8   9   10

Warning signs (hours to days prior)?

- Mood change
- Decreased concentration
- Visual disturbance
- Physical symptoms
- Fatigue
- Sensitivity to light, sounds, or smells
- Neck discomfort
- Difficult speaking/reading
- Nausea
- Change in bowel habits
- Food cravings/thirst
- Yawning
- Other:_____

Headache symptoms?

- Pain on one side
- Pain on both sides
- Throbbing pain
- Constant pain
- Sensitive to light
- Sensitive to sound
- Worse with movement
- Nausea/vomiting
- Nasal congestion
- Feeling cold or warm
- Sensitive to smell/touch
- Neck pain
- Visual or other physical symptoms
- Other:_____

Potential triggers?

- Diet change
- Change in water/caffeine/alcohol intake
- Decreased sleep
- Medication change
- Increased stress
- Weather
- Amount of light
- Strong smells
- Loud sounds
- Hormone change
- Pressure on head
- Vitamin/mineral deficiency
- Change in exercise
- Travel
- Other:_____

Feelings afterward?

- Feel normal
- Depressed
- Very happy
- Fatigued
- Decreased concentration
- Other:_____

Additional details of headache:

Date:_____ Time:_____

How long did the headache last:_____

How severe is the pain? (Circle a number)

1   2   3   4   5   6   7   8   9   10

Warning signs (hours to days prior)?

- ○ Mood change
- ○ Decreased concentration
- ○ Visual disturbance
- ○ Physical symptoms
- ○ Fatigue
- ○ Sensitivity to light, sounds, or smells
- ○ Neck discomfort
- ○ Difficult speaking/reading
- ○ Nausea
- ○ Change in bowel habits
- ○ Food cravings/thirst
- ○ Yawning
- ○ Other:_____

Headache symptoms?

- ○ Pain on one side
- ○ Pain on both sides
- ○ Throbbing pain
- ○ Constant pain
- ○ Sensitive to light
- ○ Sensitive to sound
- ○ Worse with movement
- ○ Nausea/vomiting
- ○ Nasal congestion
- ○ Feeling cold or warm
- ○ Sensitive to smell/touch
- ○ Neck pain
- ○ Visual or other physical symptoms
- ○ Other:_____

Potential triggers?

- ○ Diet change
- ○ Change in water/caffeine/alcohol intake
- ○ Decreased sleep
- ○ Medication change
- ○ Increased stress
- ○ Weather
- ○ Amount of light
- ○ Strong smells
- ○ Loud sounds
- ○ Hormone change
- ○ Pressure on head
- ○ Vitamin/mineral deficiency
- ○ Change in exercise
- ○ Travel
- ○ Other:_____

Feelings afterward?

- ○ Feel normal
- ○ Depressed
- ○ Very happy
- ○ Fatigued
- ○ Decreased concentration
- ○ Other:_____

Additional details of headache:

Date:_____ Time:_____

How long did the headache last:_____

How severe is the pain? (Circle a number)

1   2   3   4   5   6   7   8   9   10

Warning signs (hours to days prior)?

- Mood change
- Decreased concentration
- Visual disturbance
- Physical symptoms
- Fatigue
- Sensitivity to light, sounds, or smells
- Neck discomfort
- Difficult speaking/reading
- Nausea
- Change in bowel habits
- Food cravings/thirst
- Yawning
- Other:_____

Headache symptoms?

- Pain on one side
- Pain on both sides
- Throbbing pain
- Constant pain
- Sensitive to light
- Sensitive to sound
- Worse with movement
- Nausea/vomiting
- Nasal congestion
- Feeling cold or warm
- Sensitive to smell/touch
- Neck pain
- Visual or other physical symptoms
- Other:_____

Potential triggers?

- Diet change
- Change in water/caffeine/alcohol intake
- Decreased sleep
- Medication change
- Increased stress
- Weather
- Amount of light
- Strong smells
- Loud sounds
- Hormone change
- Pressure on head
- Vitamin/mineral deficiency
- Change in exercise
- Travel
- Other:_____

Feelings afterward?

- Feel normal
- Depressed
- Very happy
- Fatigued
- Decreased concentration
- Other:_____

Additional details of headache:

Date:_____ Time:_____

How long did the headache last:_____

How severe is the pain? (Circle a number)

1 2 3 4 5 6 7 8 9 10

Warning signs (hours to days prior)?

- Mood change
- Decreased concentration
- Visual disturbance
- Physical symptoms
- Fatigue
- Sensitivity to light, sounds, or smells
- Neck discomfort
- Difficult speaking/reading
- Nausea
- Change in bowel habits
- Food cravings/thirst
- Yawning
- Other:_____

Headache symptoms?

- Pain on one side
- Pain on both sides
- Throbbing pain
- Constant pain
- Sensitive to light
- Sensitive to sound
- Worse with movement
- Nausea/vomiting
- Nasal congestion
- Feeling cold or warm
- Sensitive to smell/touch
- Neck pain
- Visual or other physical symptoms
- Other:_____

Potential triggers?

- Diet change
- Change in water/caffeine/alcohol intake
- Decreased sleep
- Medication change
- Increased stress
- Weather
- Amount of light
- Strong smells
- Loud sounds
- Hormone change
- Pressure on head
- Vitamin/mineral deficiency
- Change in exercise
- Travel
- Other:_____

Feelings afterward?

- Feel normal
- Depressed
- Very happy
- Fatigued
- Decreased concentration
- Other:_____

Additional details of headache:

Date:_____ Time:_____

How long did the headache last:_____

How severe is the pain? (Circle a number)

1   2   3   4   5   6   7   8   9   10

Warning signs (hours to days prior)?

- Mood change
- Decreased concentration
- Visual disturbance
- Physical symptoms
- Fatigue
- Sensitivity to light, sounds, or smells
- Neck discomfort
- Difficult speaking/reading
- Nausea
- Change in bowel habits
- Food cravings/thirst
- Yawning
- Other:_____

Headache symptoms?

- Pain on one side
- Pain on both sides
- Throbbing pain
- Constant pain
- Sensitive to light
- Sensitive to sound
- Worse with movement
- Nausea/vomiting
- Nasal congestion
- Feeling cold or warm
- Sensitive to smell/touch
- Neck pain
- Visual or other physical symptoms
- Other:_____

Potential triggers?

- Diet change
- Change in water/caffeine/alcohol intake
- Decreased sleep
- Medication change
- Increased stress
- Weather
- Amount of light
- Strong smells
- Loud sounds
- Hormone change
- Pressure on head
- Vitamin/mineral deficiency
- Change in exercise
- Travel
- Other:_____

Feelings afterward?

- Feel normal
- Depressed
- Very happy
- Fatigued
- Decreased concentration
- Other:_____

Additional details of headache:

Date:_____ Time:_____

How long did the headache last:_____

How severe is the pain? (Circle a number)

1 2 3 4 5 6 7 8 9 10

Warning signs (hours to days prior)?

- Mood change
- Decreased concentration
- Visual disturbance
- Physical symptoms
- Fatigue
- Sensitivity to light, sounds, or smells
- Neck discomfort
- Difficult speaking/reading
- Nausea
- Change in bowel habits
- Food cravings/thirst
- Yawning
- Other:_____

Headache symptoms?

- Pain on one side
- Pain on both sides
- Throbbing pain
- Constant pain
- Sensitive to light
- Sensitive to sound
- Worse with movement
- Nausea/vomiting
- Nasal congestion
- Feeling cold or warm
- Sensitive to smell/touch
- Neck pain
- Visual or other physical symptoms
- Other:_____

Potential triggers?

- Diet change
- Change in water/caffeine/alcohol intake
- Decreased sleep
- Medication change
- Increased stress
- Weather
- Amount of light
- Strong smells
- Loud sounds
- Hormone change
- Pressure on head
- Vitamin/mineral deficiency
- Change in exercise
- Travel
- Other:_____

Feelings afterward?

- Feel normal
- Depressed
- Very happy
- Fatigued
- Decreased concentration
- Other:_____

Additional details of headache:

Date:_____ Time:_____

How long did the headache last:_____

How severe is the pain? (Circle a number)

1   2   3   4   5   6   7   8   9   10

Warning signs (hours to days prior)?

- Mood change
- Decreased concentration
- Visual disturbance
- Physical symptoms
- Fatigue
- Sensitivity to light, sounds, or smells
- Neck discomfort
- Difficult speaking/reading
- Nausea
- Change in bowel habits
- Food cravings/thirst
- Yawning
- Other:_____

Headache symptoms?

- Pain on one side
- Pain on both sides
- Throbbing pain
- Constant pain
- Sensitive to light
- Sensitive to sound
- Worse with movement
- Nausea/vomiting
- Nasal congestion
- Feeling cold or warm
- Sensitive to smell/touch
- Neck pain
- Visual or other physical symptoms
- Other:_____

Potential triggers?

- Diet change
- Change in water/caffeine/alcohol intake
- Decreased sleep
- Medication change
- Increased stress
- Weather
- Amount of light
- Strong smells
- Loud sounds
- Hormone change
- Pressure on head
- Vitamin/mineral deficiency
- Change in exercise
- Travel
- Other:_____

Feelings afterward?

- Feel normal
- Depressed
- Very happy
- Fatigued
- Decreased concentration
- Other:_____

Additional details of headache:

Date:_____ Time:_____

How long did the headache last:_____

How severe is the pain? (Circle a number)

1   2   3   4   5   6   7   8   9   10

Warning signs (hours to days prior)?

- ○ Mood change
- ○ Decreased concentration
- ○ Visual disturbance
- ○ Physical symptoms
- ○ Fatigue
- ○ Sensitivity to light, sounds, or smells
- ○ Neck discomfort
- ○ Difficult speaking/reading
- ○ Nausea
- ○ Change in bowel habits
- ○ Food cravings/thirst
- ○ Yawning
- ○ Other:_____

Headache symptoms?

- ○ Pain on one side
- ○ Pain on both sides
- ○ Throbbing pain
- ○ Constant pain
- ○ Sensitive to light
- ○ Sensitive to sound
- ○ Worse with movement
- ○ Nausea/vomiting
- ○ Nasal congestion
- ○ Feeling cold or warm
- ○ Sensitive to smell/touch
- ○ Neck pain
- ○ Visual or other physical symptoms
- ○ Other:_____

Potential triggers?

- ○ Diet change
- ○ Change in water/caffeine/alcohol intake
- ○ Decreased sleep
- ○ Medication change
- ○ Increased stress
- ○ Weather
- ○ Amount of light
- ○ Strong smells
- ○ Loud sounds
- ○ Hormone change
- ○ Pressure on head
- ○ Vitamin/mineral deficiency
- ○ Change in exercise
- ○ Travel
- ○ Other:_____

Feelings afterward?

- ○ Feel normal
- ○ Depressed
- ○ Very happy
- ○ Fatigued
- ○ Decreased concentration
- ○ Other:_____

Additional details of headache:

Date:_____ Time:_____

How long did the headache last:_____

How severe is the pain? (Circle a number)

1   2   3   4   5   6   7   8   9   10

Warning signs (hours to days prior)?

- Mood change
- Decreased concentration
- Visual disturbance
- Physical symptoms
- Fatigue
- Sensitivity to light, sounds, or smells
- Neck discomfort
- Difficult speaking/reading
- Nausea
- Change in bowel habits
- Food cravings/thirst
- Yawning
- Other:_____

Headache symptoms?

- Pain on one side
- Pain on both sides
- Throbbing pain
- Constant pain
- Sensitive to light
- Sensitive to sound
- Worse with movement
- Nausea/vomiting
- Nasal congestion
- Feeling cold or warm
- Sensitive to smell/touch
- Neck pain
- Visual or other physical symptoms
- Other:_____

Potential triggers?

- Diet change
- Change in water/caffeine/alcohol intake
- Decreased sleep
- Medication change
- Increased stress
- Weather
- Amount of light
- Strong smells
- Loud sounds
- Hormone change
- Pressure on head
- Vitamin/mineral deficiency
- Change in exercise
- Travel
- Other:_____

Feelings afterward?

- Feel normal
- Depressed
- Very happy
- Fatigued
- Decreased concentration
- Other:_____

Additional details of headache:

Date:_____ Time:_____

How long did the headache last:_____

How severe is the pain? (Circle a number)

1   2   3   4   5   6   7   8   9   10

Warning signs (hours to days prior)?

- Mood change
- Decreased concentration
- Visual disturbance
- Physical symptoms
- Fatigue
- Sensitivity to light, sounds, or smells
- Neck discomfort
- Difficult speaking/reading
- Nausea
- Change in bowel habits
- Food cravings/thirst
- Yawning
- Other:_____

Headache symptoms?

- Pain on one side
- Pain on both sides
- Throbbing pain
- Constant pain
- Sensitive to light
- Sensitive to sound
- Worse with movement
- Nausea/vomiting
- Nasal congestion
- Feeling cold or warm
- Sensitive to smell/touch
- Neck pain
- Visual or other physical symptoms
- Other:_____

Potential triggers?

- Diet change
- Change in water/caffeine/alcohol intake
- Decreased sleep
- Medication change
- Increased stress
- Weather
- Amount of light
- Strong smells
- Loud sounds
- Hormone change
- Pressure on head
- Vitamin/mineral deficiency
- Change in exercise
- Travel
- Other:_____

Feelings afterward?

- Feel normal
- Depressed
- Very happy
- Fatigued
- Decreased concentration
- Other:_____

Additional details of headache:

Date:_____ Time:_____

How long did the headache last:_____

How severe is the pain? (Circle a number)

1 2 3 4 5 6 7 8 9 10

Warning signs (hours to days prior)?

- Mood change
- Decreased concentration
- Visual disturbance
- Physical symptoms
- Fatigue
- Sensitivity to light, sounds, or smells
- Neck discomfort
- Difficult speaking/reading
- Nausea
- Change in bowel habits
- Food cravings/thirst
- Yawning
- Other:_____

Headache symptoms?

- Pain on one side
- Pain on both sides
- Throbbing pain
- Constant pain
- Sensitive to light
- Sensitive to sound
- Worse with movement
- Nausea/vomiting
- Nasal congestion
- Feeling cold or warm
- Sensitive to smell/touch
- Neck pain
- Visual or other physical symptoms
- Other:_____

Potential triggers?

- Diet change
- Change in water/caffeine/alcohol intake
- Decreased sleep
- Medication change
- Increased stress
- Weather
- Amount of light
- Strong smells
- Loud sounds
- Hormone change
- Pressure on head
- Vitamin/mineral deficiency
- Change in exercise
- Travel
- Other:_____

Feelings afterward?

- Feel normal
- Depressed
- Very happy
- Fatigued
- Decreased concentration
- Other:_____

Additional details of headache:

Date:_____ Time:_____

How long did the headache last:_____

How severe is the pain? (Circle a number)

1 2 3 4 5 6 7 8 9 10

Warning signs (hours to days prior)?

- Mood change
- Decreased concentration
- Visual disturbance
- Physical symptoms
- Fatigue
- Sensitivity to light, sounds, or smells
- Neck discomfort
- Difficult speaking/reading
- Nausea
- Change in bowel habits
- Food cravings/thirst
- Yawning
- Other:_____

Headache symptoms?

- Pain on one side
- Pain on both sides
- Throbbing pain
- Constant pain
- Sensitive to light
- Sensitive to sound
- Worse with movement
- Nausea/vomiting
- Nasal congestion
- Feeling cold or warm
- Sensitive to smell/touch
- Neck pain
- Visual or other physical symptoms
- Other:_____

Potential triggers?

- Diet change
- Change in water/caffeine/alcohol intake
- Decreased sleep
- Medication change
- Increased stress
- Weather
- Amount of light
- Strong smells
- Loud sounds
- Hormone change
- Pressure on head
- Vitamin/mineral deficiency
- Change in exercise
- Travel
- Other:_____

Feelings afterward?

- Feel normal
- Depressed
- Very happy
- Fatigued
- Decreased concentration
- Other:_____

Additional details of headache:

Date:_____ Time:_____

How long did the headache last:_____

How severe is the pain? (Circle a number)

1   2   3   4   5   6   7   8   9   10

Warning signs (hours to days prior)?

- Mood change
- Decreased concentration
- Visual disturbance
- Physical symptoms
- Fatigue
- Sensitivity to light, sounds, or smells
- Neck discomfort
- Difficult speaking/reading
- Nausea
- Change in bowel habits
- Food cravings/thirst
- Yawning
- Other:_____

Headache symptoms?

- Pain on one side
- Pain on both sides
- Throbbing pain
- Constant pain
- Sensitive to light
- Sensitive to sound
- Worse with movement
- Nausea/vomiting
- Nasal congestion
- Feeling cold or warm
- Sensitive to smell/touch
- Neck pain
- Visual or other physical symptoms
- Other:_____

Potential triggers?

- Diet change
- Change in water/caffeine/alcohol intake
- Decreased sleep
- Medication change
- Increased stress
- Weather
- Amount of light
- Strong smells
- Loud sounds
- Hormone change
- Pressure on head
- Vitamin/mineral deficiency
- Change in exercise
- Travel
- Other:_____

Feelings afterward?

- Feel normal
- Depressed
- Very happy
- Fatigued
- Decreased concentration
- Other:_____

Additional details of headache:

Date:_____ Time:_____

How long did the headache last:_____

How severe is the pain? (Circle a number)

1   2   3   4   5   6   7   8   9   10

Warning signs (hours to days prior)?

- ○ Mood change
- ○ Decreased concentration
- ○ Visual disturbance
- ○ Physical symptoms
- ○ Fatigue
- ○ Sensitivity to light, sounds, or smells
- ○ Neck discomfort
- ○ Difficult speaking/reading
- ○ Nausea
- ○ Change in bowel habits
- ○ Food cravings/thirst
- ○ Yawning
- ○ Other:_____

Headache symptoms?

- ○ Pain on one side
- ○ Pain on both sides
- ○ Throbbing pain
- ○ Constant pain
- ○ Sensitive to light
- ○ Sensitive to sound
- ○ Worse with movement
- ○ Nausea/vomiting
- ○ Nasal congestion
- ○ Feeling cold or warm
- ○ Sensitive to smell/touch
- ○ Neck pain
- ○ Visual or other physical symptoms
- ○ Other:_____

Potential triggers?

- ○ Diet change
- ○ Change in water/caffeine/alcohol intake
- ○ Decreased sleep
- ○ Medication change
- ○ Increased stress
- ○ Weather
- ○ Amount of light
- ○ Strong smells
- ○ Loud sounds
- ○ Hormone change
- ○ Pressure on head
- ○ Vitamin/mineral deficiency
- ○ Change in exercise
- ○ Travel
- ○ Other:_____

Feelings afterward?

- ○ Feel normal
- ○ Depressed
- ○ Very happy
- ○ Fatigued
- ○ Decreased concentration
- ○ Other:_____

Additional details of headache:

Date:_____ Time:_____

How long did the headache last:_____

How severe is the pain? (Circle a number)

1 2 3 4 5 6 7 8 9 10

Warning signs (hours to days prior)?

- Mood change
- Decreased concentration
- Visual disturbance
- Physical symptoms
- Fatigue
- Sensitivity to light, sounds, or smells
- Neck discomfort
- Difficult speaking/reading
- Nausea
- Change in bowel habits
- Food cravings/thirst
- Yawning
- Other:_____

Headache symptoms?

- Pain on one side
- Pain on both sides
- Throbbing pain
- Constant pain
- Sensitive to light
- Sensitive to sound
- Worse with movement
- Nausea/vomiting
- Nasal congestion
- Feeling cold or warm
- Sensitive to smell/touch
- Neck pain
- Visual or other physical symptoms
- Other:_____

Potential triggers?

- Diet change
- Change in water/caffeine/alcohol intake
- Decreased sleep
- Medication change
- Increased stress
- Weather
- Amount of light
- Strong smells
- Loud sounds
- Hormone change
- Pressure on head
- Vitamin/mineral deficiency
- Change in exercise
- Travel
- Other:_____

Feelings afterward?

- Feel normal
- Depressed
- Very happy
- Fatigued
- Decreased concentration
- Other:_____

Additional details of headache:

Date:_____ Time:_____

How long did the headache last:_____

How severe is the pain? (Circle a number)

1 2 3 4 5 6 7 8 9 10

Warning signs (hours to days prior)?

- ○ Mood change
- ○ Decreased concentration
- ○ Visual disturbance
- ○ Physical symptoms
- ○ Fatigue
- ○ Sensitivity to light, sounds, or smells
- ○ Neck discomfort
- ○ Difficult speaking/reading
- ○ Nausea
- ○ Change in bowel habits
- ○ Food cravings/thirst
- ○ Yawning
- ○ Other:_____

Headache symptoms?

- ○ Pain on one side
- ○ Pain on both sides
- ○ Throbbing pain
- ○ Constant pain
- ○ Sensitive to light
- ○ Sensitive to sound
- ○ Worse with movement
- ○ Nausea/vomiting
- ○ Nasal congestion
- ○ Feeling cold or warm
- ○ Sensitive to smell/touch
- ○ Neck pain
- ○ Visual or other physical symptoms
- ○ Other:_____

Potential triggers?

- ○ Diet change
- ○ Change in water/caffeine/alcohol intake
- ○ Decreased sleep
- ○ Medication change
- ○ Increased stress
- ○ Weather
- ○ Amount of light
- ○ Strong smells
- ○ Loud sounds
- ○ Hormone change
- ○ Pressure on head
- ○ Vitamin/mineral deficiency
- ○ Change in exercise
- ○ Travel
- ○ Other:_____

Feelings afterward?

- ○ Feel normal
- ○ Depressed
- ○ Very happy
- ○ Fatigued
- ○ Decreased concentration
- ○ Other:_____

Additional details of headache:

Date:_____ Time:_____

How long did the headache last:_____

How severe is the pain? (Circle a number)

1 2 3 4 5 6 7 8 9 10

Warning signs (hours to days prior)?

- Mood change
- Decreased concentration
- Visual disturbance
- Physical symptoms
- Fatigue
- Sensitivity to light, sounds, or smells
- Neck discomfort
- Difficult speaking/reading
- Nausea
- Change in bowel habits
- Food cravings/thirst
- Yawning
- Other:_____

Headache symptoms?

- Pain on one side
- Pain on both sides
- Throbbing pain
- Constant pain
- Sensitive to light
- Sensitive to sound
- Worse with movement
- Nausea/vomiting
- Nasal congestion
- Feeling cold or warm
- Sensitive to smell/touch
- Neck pain
- Visual or other physical symptoms
- Other:_____

Potential triggers?

- Diet change
- Change in water/caffeine/alcohol intake
- Decreased sleep
- Medication change
- Increased stress
- Weather
- Amount of light
- Strong smells
- Loud sounds
- Hormone change
- Pressure on head
- Vitamin/mineral deficiency
- Change in exercise
- Travel
- Other:_____

Feelings afterward?

- Feel normal
- Depressed
- Very happy
- Fatigued
- Decreased concentration
- Other:_____

Additional details of headache:

Date:_____ Time:_____

How long did the headache last:_____

How severe is the pain? (Circle a number)

1   2   3   4   5   6   7   8   9   10

Warning signs (hours to days prior)?

- ○ Mood change
- ○ Decreased concentration
- ○ Visual disturbance
- ○ Physical symptoms
- ○ Fatigue
- ○ Sensitivity to light, sounds, or smells
- ○ Neck discomfort
- ○ Difficult speaking/reading
- ○ Nausea
- ○ Change in bowel habits
- ○ Food cravings/thirst
- ○ Yawning
- ○ Other:_____

Headache symptoms?

- ○ Pain on one side
- ○ Pain on both sides
- ○ Throbbing pain
- ○ Constant pain
- ○ Sensitive to light
- ○ Sensitive to sound
- ○ Worse with movement
- ○ Nausea/vomiting
- ○ Nasal congestion
- ○ Feeling cold or warm
- ○ Sensitive to smell/touch
- ○ Neck pain
- ○ Visual or other physical symptoms
- ○ Other:_____

Potential triggers?

- ○ Diet change
- ○ Change in water/caffeine/alcohol intake
- ○ Decreased sleep
- ○ Medication change
- ○ Increased stress
- ○ Weather
- ○ Amount of light
- ○ Strong smells
- ○ Loud sounds
- ○ Hormone change
- ○ Pressure on head
- ○ Vitamin/mineral deficiency
- ○ Change in exercise
- ○ Travel
- ○ Other:_____

Feelings afterward?

- ○ Feel normal
- ○ Depressed
- ○ Very happy
- ○ Fatigued
- ○ Decreased concentration
- ○ Other:_____

Additional details of headache:

Date:_____ Time:_____

How long did the headache last:_____

How severe is the pain? (Circle a number)

1 2 3 4 5 6 7 8 9 10

Warning signs (hours to days prior)?

- Mood change
- Decreased concentration
- Visual disturbance
- Physical symptoms
- Fatigue
- Sensitivity to light, sounds, or smells
- Neck discomfort
- Difficult speaking/reading
- Nausea
- Change in bowel habits
- Food cravings/thirst
- Yawning
- Other:_____

Headache symptoms?

- Pain on one side
- Pain on both sides
- Throbbing pain
- Constant pain
- Sensitive to light
- Sensitive to sound
- Worse with movement
- Nausea/vomiting
- Nasal congestion
- Feeling cold or warm
- Sensitive to smell/touch
- Neck pain
- Visual or other physical symptoms
- Other:_____

Potential triggers?

- Diet change
- Change in water/caffeine/alcohol intake
- Decreased sleep
- Medication change
- Increased stress
- Weather
- Amount of light
- Strong smells
- Loud sounds
- Hormone change
- Pressure on head
- Vitamin/mineral deficiency
- Change in exercise
- Travel
- Other:_____

Feelings afterward?

- Feel normal
- Depressed
- Very happy
- Fatigued
- Decreased concentration
- Other:_____

Additional details of headache:

Date:_____ Time:_____

How long did the headache last:_____

How severe is the pain? (Circle a number)

1   2   3   4   5   6   7   8   9   10

Warning signs (hours to days prior)?

○ Mood change
○ Decreased concentration
○ Visual disturbance
○ Physical symptoms
○ Fatigue
○ Sensitivity to light, sounds, or smells
○ Neck discomfort
○ Difficult speaking/reading
○ Nausea
○ Change in bowel habits
○ Food cravings/thirst
○ Yawning
○ Other:_____

Headache symptoms?

○ Pain on one side
○ Pain on both sides
○ Throbbing pain
○ Constant pain
○ Sensitive to light
○ Sensitive to sound
○ Worse with movement
○ Nausea/vomiting
○ Nasal congestion
○ Feeling cold or warm
○ Sensitive to smell/touch
○ Neck pain
○ Visual or other physical symptoms
○ Other:_____

Potential triggers?

○ Diet change
○ Change in water/caffeine/alcohol intake
○ Decreased sleep
○ Medication change
○ Increased stress
○ Weather
○ Amount of light
○ Strong smells
○ Loud sounds
○ Hormone change
○ Pressure on head
○ Vitamin/mineral deficiency
○ Change in exercise
○ Travel
○ Other:_____

Feelings afterward?

○ Feel normal
○ Depressed
○ Very happy
○ Fatigued
○ Decreased concentration
○ Other:_____

Additional details of headache:

Date:_____ Time:_____

How long did the headache last:_____

How severe is the pain? (Circle a number)

1   2   3   4   5   6   7   8   9   10

Warning signs (hours to days prior)?

- Mood change
- Decreased concentration
- Visual disturbance
- Physical symptoms
- Fatigue
- Sensitivity to light, sounds, or smells
- Neck discomfort
- Difficult speaking/reading
- Nausea
- Change in bowel habits
- Food cravings/thirst
- Yawning
- Other:_____

Headache symptoms?

- Pain on one side
- Pain on both sides
- Throbbing pain
- Constant pain
- Sensitive to light
- Sensitive to sound
- Worse with movement
- Nausea/vomiting
- Nasal congestion
- Feeling cold or warm
- Sensitive to smell/touch
- Neck pain
- Visual or other physical symptoms
- Other:_____

Potential triggers?

- Diet change
- Change in water/caffeine/alcohol intake
- Decreased sleep
- Medication change
- Increased stress
- Weather
- Amount of light
- Strong smells
- Loud sounds
- Hormone change
- Pressure on head
- Vitamin/mineral deficiency
- Change in exercise
- Travel
- Other:_____

Feelings afterward?

- Feel normal
- Depressed
- Very happy
- Fatigued
- Decreased concentration
- Other:_____

Additional details of headache:

Date:_____ Time:_____

How long did the headache last:_____

How severe is the pain? (Circle a number)

1 2 3 4 5 6 7 8 9 10

Warning signs (hours to days prior)?

- ○ Mood change
- ○ Decreased concentration
- ○ Visual disturbance
- ○ Physical symptoms
- ○ Fatigue
- ○ Sensitivity to light, sounds, or smells
- ○ Neck discomfort
- ○ Difficult speaking/reading
- ○ Nausea
- ○ Change in bowel habits
- ○ Food cravings/thirst
- ○ Yawning
- ○ Other:_____

Headache symptoms?

- ○ Pain on one side
- ○ Pain on both sides
- ○ Throbbing pain
- ○ Constant pain
- ○ Sensitive to light
- ○ Sensitive to sound
- ○ Worse with movement
- ○ Nausea/vomiting
- ○ Nasal congestion
- ○ Feeling cold or warm
- ○ Sensitive to smell/touch
- ○ Neck pain
- ○ Visual or other physical symptoms
- ○ Other:_____

Potential triggers?

- ○ Diet change
- ○ Change in water/caffeine/alcohol intake
- ○ Decreased sleep
- ○ Medication change
- ○ Increased stress
- ○ Weather
- ○ Amount of light
- ○ Strong smells
- ○ Loud sounds
- ○ Hormone change
- ○ Pressure on head
- ○ Vitamin/mineral deficiency
- ○ Change in exercise
- ○ Travel
- ○ Other:_____

Feelings afterward?

- ○ Feel normal
- ○ Depressed
- ○ Very happy
- ○ Fatigued
- ○ Decreased concentration
- ○ Other:_____

Additional details of headache:

Date:_____ Time:_____

How long did the headache last:_____

How severe is the pain? (Circle a number)

1   2   3   4   5   6   7   8   9   10

Warning signs (hours to days prior)?

- Mood change
- Decreased concentration
- Visual disturbance
- Physical symptoms
- Fatigue
- Sensitivity to light, sounds, or smells
- Neck discomfort
- Difficult speaking/reading
- Nausea
- Change in bowel habits
- Food cravings/thirst
- Yawning
- Other:_____

Headache symptoms?

- Pain on one side
- Pain on both sides
- Throbbing pain
- Constant pain
- Sensitive to light
- Sensitive to sound
- Worse with movement
- Nausea/vomiting
- Nasal congestion
- Feeling cold or warm
- Sensitive to smell/touch
- Neck pain
- Visual or other physical symptoms
- Other:_____

Potential triggers?

- Diet change
- Change in water/caffeine/alcohol intake
- Decreased sleep
- Medication change
- Increased stress
- Weather
- Amount of light
- Strong smells
- Loud sounds
- Hormone change
- Pressure on head
- Vitamin/mineral deficiency
- Change in exercise
- Travel
- Other:_____

Feelings afterward?

- Feel normal
- Depressed
- Very happy
- Fatigued
- Decreased concentration
- Other:_____

Additional details of headache:

Date:_____ Time:_____

How long did the headache last:_____

How severe is the pain? (Circle a number)

1   2   3   4   5   6   7   8   9   10

Warning signs (hours to days prior)?

- ○ Mood change
- ○ Decreased concentration
- ○ Visual disturbance
- ○ Physical symptoms
- ○ Fatigue
- ○ Sensitivity to light, sounds, or smells
- ○ Neck discomfort
- ○ Difficult speaking/reading
- ○ Nausea
- ○ Change in bowel habits
- ○ Food cravings/thirst
- ○ Yawning
- ○ Other:_____

Headache symptoms?

- ○ Pain on one side
- ○ Pain on both sides
- ○ Throbbing pain
- ○ Constant pain
- ○ Sensitive to light
- ○ Sensitive to sound
- ○ Worse with movement
- ○ Nausea/vomiting
- ○ Nasal congestion
- ○ Feeling cold or warm
- ○ Sensitive to smell/touch
- ○ Neck pain
- ○ Visual or other physical symptoms
- ○ Other:_____

Potential triggers?

- ○ Diet change
- ○ Change in water/caffeine/alcohol intake
- ○ Decreased sleep
- ○ Medication change
- ○ Increased stress
- ○ Weather
- ○ Amount of light
- ○ Strong smells
- ○ Loud sounds
- ○ Hormone change
- ○ Pressure on head
- ○ Vitamin/mineral deficiency
- ○ Change in exercise
- ○ Travel
- ○ Other:_____

Feelings afterward?

- ○ Feel normal
- ○ Depressed
- ○ Very happy
- ○ Fatigued
- ○ Decreased concentration
- ○ Other:_____

Additional details of headache:

Date:_____ Time:_____

How long did the headache last:_____

How severe is the pain? (Circle a number)

1 2 3 4 5 6 7 8 9 10

Warning signs (hours to days prior)?

- Mood change
- Decreased concentration
- Visual disturbance
- Physical symptoms
- Fatigue
- Sensitivity to light, sounds, or smells
- Neck discomfort
- Difficult speaking/reading
- Nausea
- Change in bowel habits
- Food cravings/thirst
- Yawning
- Other:_____

Headache symptoms?

- Pain on one side
- Pain on both sides
- Throbbing pain
- Constant pain
- Sensitive to light
- Sensitive to sound
- Worse with movement
- Nausea/vomiting
- Nasal congestion
- Feeling cold or warm
- Sensitive to smell/touch
- Neck pain
- Visual or other physical symptoms
- Other:_____

Potential triggers?

- Diet change
- Change in water/caffeine/alcohol intake
- Decreased sleep
- Medication change
- Increased stress
- Weather
- Amount of light
- Strong smells
- Loud sounds
- Hormone change
- Pressure on head
- Vitamin/mineral deficiency
- Change in exercise
- Travel
- Other:_____

Feelings afterward?

- Feel normal
- Depressed
- Very happy
- Fatigued
- Decreased concentration
- Other:_____

Additional details of headache:

Date:_____ Time:_____

How long did the headache last:_____

How severe is the pain? (Circle a number)

1   2   3   4   5   6   7   8   9   10

Warning signs (hours to days prior)?

- ○ Mood change
- ○ Decreased concentration
- ○ Visual disturbance
- ○ Physical symptoms
- ○ Fatigue
- ○ Sensitivity to light, sounds, or smells
- ○ Neck discomfort
- ○ Difficult speaking/reading
- ○ Nausea
- ○ Change in bowel habits
- ○ Food cravings/thirst
- ○ Yawning
- ○ Other:_____

Headache symptoms?

- ○ Pain on one side
- ○ Pain on both sides
- ○ Throbbing pain
- ○ Constant pain
- ○ Sensitive to light
- ○ Sensitive to sound
- ○ Worse with movement
- ○ Nausea/vomiting
- ○ Nasal congestion
- ○ Feeling cold or warm
- ○ Sensitive to smell/touch
- ○ Neck pain
- ○ Visual or other physical symptoms
- ○ Other:_____

Potential triggers?

- ○ Diet change
- ○ Change in water/caffeine/alcohol intake
- ○ Decreased sleep
- ○ Medication change
- ○ Increased stress
- ○ Weather
- ○ Amount of light
- ○ Strong smells
- ○ Loud sounds
- ○ Hormone change
- ○ Pressure on head
- ○ Vitamin/mineral deficiency
- ○ Change in exercise
- ○ Travel
- ○ Other:_____

Feelings afterward?

- ○ Feel normal
- ○ Depressed
- ○ Very happy
- ○ Fatigued
- ○ Decreased concentration
- ○ Other:_____

Additional details of headache:

Date:_____ Time:_____

How long did the headache last:_____

How severe is the pain? (Circle a number)

1   2   3   4   5   6   7   8   9   10

Warning signs (hours to days prior)?

- Mood change
- Decreased concentration
- Visual disturbance
- Physical symptoms
- Fatigue
- Sensitivity to light, sounds, or smells
- Neck discomfort
- Difficult speaking/reading
- Nausea
- Change in bowel habits
- Food cravings/thirst
- Yawning
- Other:_____

Headache symptoms?

- Pain on one side
- Pain on both sides
- Throbbing pain
- Constant pain
- Sensitive to light
- Sensitive to sound
- Worse with movement
- Nausea/vomiting
- Nasal congestion
- Feeling cold or warm
- Sensitive to smell/touch
- Neck pain
- Visual or other physical symptoms
- Other:_____

Potential triggers?

- Diet change
- Change in water/caffeine/alcohol intake
- Decreased sleep
- Medication change
- Increased stress
- Weather
- Amount of light
- Strong smells
- Loud sounds
- Hormone change
- Pressure on head
- Vitamin/mineral deficiency
- Change in exercise
- Travel
- Other:_____

Feelings afterward?

- Feel normal
- Depressed
- Very happy
- Fatigued
- Decreased concentration
- Other:_____

Additional details of headache:

Date:_____ Time:_____

How long did the headache last:_____

How severe is the pain? (Circle a number)

1   2   3   4   5   6   7   8   9   10

Warning signs (hours to days prior)?

- Mood change
- Decreased concentration
- Visual disturbance
- Physical symptoms
- Fatigue
- Sensitivity to light, sounds, or smells
- Neck discomfort
- Difficult speaking/reading
- Nausea
- Change in bowel habits
- Food cravings/thirst
- Yawning
- Other:_____

Headache symptoms?

- Pain on one side
- Pain on both sides
- Throbbing pain
- Constant pain
- Sensitive to light
- Sensitive to sound
- Worse with movement
- Nausea/vomiting
- Nasal congestion
- Feeling cold or warm
- Sensitive to smell/touch
- Neck pain
- Visual or other physical symptoms
- Other:_____

Potential triggers?

- Diet change
- Change in water/caffeine/alcohol intake
- Decreased sleep
- Medication change
- Increased stress
- Weather
- Amount of light
- Strong smells
- Loud sounds
- Hormone change
- Pressure on head
- Vitamin/mineral deficiency
- Change in exercise
- Travel
- Other:_____

Feelings afterward?

- Feel normal
- Depressed
- Very happy
- Fatigued
- Decreased concentration
- Other:_____

Additional details of headache:

Date:_____ Time:_____

How long did the headache last:_____

How severe is the pain? (Circle a number)

1   2   3   4   5   6   7   8   9   10

Warning signs (hours to days prior)?

- Mood change
- Decreased concentration
- Visual disturbance
- Physical symptoms
- Fatigue
- Sensitivity to light, sounds, or smells
- Neck discomfort
- Difficult speaking/reading
- Nausea
- Change in bowel habits
- Food cravings/thirst
- Yawning
- Other:_____

Headache symptoms?

- Pain on one side
- Pain on both sides
- Throbbing pain
- Constant pain
- Sensitive to light
- Sensitive to sound
- Worse with movement
- Nausea/vomiting
- Nasal congestion
- Feeling cold or warm
- Sensitive to smell/touch
- Neck pain
- Visual or other physical symptoms
- Other:_____

Additional details of headache:

Potential triggers?

- Diet change
- Change in water/caffeine/alcohol intake
- Decreased sleep
- Medication change
- Increased stress
- Weather
- Amount of light
- Strong smells
- Loud sounds
- Hormone change
- Pressure on head
- Vitamin/mineral deficiency
- Change in exercise
- Travel
- Other:_____

Feelings afterward?

- Feel normal
- Depressed
- Very happy
- Fatigued
- Decreased concentration
- Other:_____

Date:_____ Time:_____

How long did the headache last:_____

How severe is the pain? (Circle a number)

1 2 3 4 5 6 7 8 9 10

Warning signs (hours to days prior)?

- Mood change
- Decreased concentration
- Visual disturbance
- Physical symptoms
- Fatigue
- Sensitivity to light, sounds, or smells
- Neck discomfort
- Difficult speaking/reading
- Nausea
- Change in bowel habits
- Food cravings/thirst
- Yawning
- Other:_____

Headache symptoms?

- Pain on one side
- Pain on both sides
- Throbbing pain
- Constant pain
- Sensitive to light
- Sensitive to sound
- Worse with movement
- Nausea/vomiting
- Nasal congestion
- Feeling cold or warm
- Sensitive to smell/touch
- Neck pain
- Visual or other physical symptoms
- Other:_____

Potential triggers?

- Diet change
- Change in water/caffeine/alcohol intake
- Decreased sleep
- Medication change
- Increased stress
- Weather
- Amount of light
- Strong smells
- Loud sounds
- Hormone change
- Pressure on head
- Vitamin/mineral deficiency
- Change in exercise
- Travel
- Other:_____

Feelings afterward?

- Feel normal
- Depressed
- Very happy
- Fatigued
- Decreased concentration
- Other:_____

Additional details of headache:

Date:_____ Time:_____

How long did the headache last:_____

How severe is the pain? (Circle a number)

1 2 3 4 5 6 7 8 9 10

Warning signs (hours to days prior)?

- Mood change
- Decreased concentration
- Visual disturbance
- Physical symptoms
- Fatigue
- Sensitivity to light, sounds, or smells
- Neck discomfort
- Difficult speaking/reading
- Nausea
- Change in bowel habits
- Food cravings/thirst
- Yawning
- Other:_____

Headache symptoms?

- Pain on one side
- Pain on both sides
- Throbbing pain
- Constant pain
- Sensitive to light
- Sensitive to sound
- Worse with movement
- Nausea/vomiting
- Nasal congestion
- Feeling cold or warm
- Sensitive to smell/touch
- Neck pain
- Visual or other physical symptoms
- Other:_____

Potential triggers?

- Diet change
- Change in water/caffeine/alcohol intake
- Decreased sleep
- Medication change
- Increased stress
- Weather
- Amount of light
- Strong smells
- Loud sounds
- Hormone change
- Pressure on head
- Vitamin/mineral deficiency
- Change in exercise
- Travel
- Other:_____

Feelings afterward?

- Feel normal
- Depressed
- Very happy
- Fatigued
- Decreased concentration
- Other:_____

Additional details of headache:

Date:_____ Time:_____

How long did the headache last:_____

How severe is the pain? (Circle a number)

1   2   3   4   5   6   7   8   9   10

Warning signs (hours to days prior)?
○ Mood change
○ Decreased concentration
○ Visual disturbance
○ Physical symptoms
○ Fatigue
○ Sensitivity to light, sounds, or smells
○ Neck discomfort
○ Difficult speaking/reading
○ Nausea
○ Change in bowel habits
○ Food cravings/thirst
○ Yawning
○ Other:_____

Headache symptoms?
○ Pain on one side
○ Pain on both sides
○ Throbbing pain
○ Constant pain
○ Sensitive to light
○ Sensitive to sound
○ Worse with movement
○ Nausea/vomiting
○ Nasal congestion
○ Feeling cold or warm
○ Sensitive to smell/touch
○ Neck pain
○ Visual or other physical symptoms
○ Other:_____

Potential triggers?
○ Diet change
○ Change in water/caffeine/alcohol intake
○ Decreased sleep
○ Medication change
○ Increased stress
○ Weather
○ Amount of light
○ Strong smells
○ Loud sounds
○ Hormone change
○ Pressure on head
○ Vitamin/mineral deficiency
○ Change in exercise
○ Travel
○ Other:_____

Feelings afterward?
○ Feel normal
○ Depressed
○ Very happy
○ Fatigued
○ Decreased concentration
○ Other:_____

Additional details of headache:

Date:_____ Time:_____

How long did the headache last:_____

How severe is the pain? (Circle a number)

1 2 3 4 5 6 7 8 9 10

Warning signs (hours to days prior)?

- Mood change
- Decreased concentration
- Visual disturbance
- Physical symptoms
- Fatigue
- Sensitivity to light, sounds, or smells
- Neck discomfort
- Difficult speaking/reading
- Nausea
- Change in bowel habits
- Food cravings/thirst
- Yawning
- Other:_____

Headache symptoms?

- Pain on one side
- Pain on both sides
- Throbbing pain
- Constant pain
- Sensitive to light
- Sensitive to sound
- Worse with movement
- Nausea/vomiting
- Nasal congestion
- Feeling cold or warm
- Sensitive to smell/touch
- Neck pain
- Visual or other physical symptoms
- Other:_____

Potential triggers?

- Diet change
- Change in water/caffeine/alcohol intake
- Decreased sleep
- Medication change
- Increased stress
- Weather
- Amount of light
- Strong smells
- Loud sounds
- Hormone change
- Pressure on head
- Vitamin/mineral deficiency
- Change in exercise
- Travel
- Other:_____

Feelings afterward?

- Feel normal
- Depressed
- Very happy
- Fatigued
- Decreased concentration
- Other:_____

Additional details of headache:

Date:_____ Time:_____

How long did the headache last:_____

How severe is the pain? (Circle a number)

1   2   3   4   5   6   7   8   9   10

Warning signs (hours to days prior)?

- ◯ Mood change
- ◯ Decreased concentration
- ◯ Visual disturbance
- ◯ Physical symptoms
- ◯ Fatigue
- ◯ Sensitivity to light, sounds, or smells
- ◯ Neck discomfort
- ◯ Difficult speaking/reading
- ◯ Nausea
- ◯ Change in bowel habits
- ◯ Food cravings/thirst
- ◯ Yawning
- ◯ Other:_____

Headache symptoms?

- ◯ Pain on one side
- ◯ Pain on both sides
- ◯ Throbbing pain
- ◯ Constant pain
- ◯ Sensitive to light
- ◯ Sensitive to sound
- ◯ Worse with movement
- ◯ Nausea/vomiting
- ◯ Nasal congestion
- ◯ Feeling cold or warm
- ◯ Sensitive to smell/touch
- ◯ Neck pain
- ◯ Visual or other physical symptoms
- ◯ Other:_____

Potential triggers?

- ◯ Diet change
- ◯ Change in water/caffeine/alcohol intake
- ◯ Decreased sleep
- ◯ Medication change
- ◯ Increased stress
- ◯ Weather
- ◯ Amount of light
- ◯ Strong smells
- ◯ Loud sounds
- ◯ Hormone change
- ◯ Pressure on head
- ◯ Vitamin/mineral deficiency
- ◯ Change in exercise
- ◯ Travel
- ◯ Other:_____

Feelings afterward?

- ◯ Feel normal
- ◯ Depressed
- ◯ Very happy
- ◯ Fatigued
- ◯ Decreased concentration
- ◯ Other:_____

Additional details of headache:

Date:_____ Time:_____

How long did the headache last:_____

How severe is the pain? (Circle a number)

1 2 3 4 5 6 7 8 9 10

Warning signs (hours to days prior)?

- Mood change
- Decreased concentration
- Visual disturbance
- Physical symptoms
- Fatigue
- Sensitivity to light, sounds, or smells
- Neck discomfort
- Difficult speaking/reading
- Nausea
- Change in bowel habits
- Food cravings/thirst
- Yawning
- Other:_____

Headache symptoms?

- Pain on one side
- Pain on both sides
- Throbbing pain
- Constant pain
- Sensitive to light
- Sensitive to sound
- Worse with movement
- Nausea/vomiting
- Nasal congestion
- Feeling cold or warm
- Sensitive to smell/touch
- Neck pain
- Visual or other physical symptoms
- Other:_____

Potential triggers?

- Diet change
- Change in water/caffeine/alcohol intake
- Decreased sleep
- Medication change
- Increased stress
- Weather
- Amount of light
- Strong smells
- Loud sounds
- Hormone change
- Pressure on head
- Vitamin/mineral deficiency
- Change in exercise
- Travel
- Other:_____

Feelings afterward?

- Feel normal
- Depressed
- Very happy
- Fatigued
- Decreased concentration
- Other:_____

Additional details of headache:

Date:_____ Time:_____

How long did the headache last:_____

How severe is the pain? (Circle a number)

1   2   3   4   5   6   7   8   9   10

Warning signs (hours to days prior)?

- ○ Mood change
- ○ Decreased concentration
- ○ Visual disturbance
- ○ Physical symptoms
- ○ Fatigue
- ○ Sensitivity to light, sounds, or smells
- ○ Neck discomfort
- ○ Difficult speaking/reading
- ○ Nausea
- ○ Change in bowel habits
- ○ Food cravings/thirst
- ○ Yawning
- ○ Other:_____

Headache symptoms?

- ○ Pain on one side
- ○ Pain on both sides
- ○ Throbbing pain
- ○ Constant pain
- ○ Sensitive to light
- ○ Sensitive to sound
- ○ Worse with movement
- ○ Nausea/vomiting
- ○ Nasal congestion
- ○ Feeling cold or warm
- ○ Sensitive to smell/touch
- ○ Neck pain
- ○ Visual or other physical symptoms
- ○ Other:_____

Potential triggers?

- ○ Diet change
- ○ Change in water/caffeine/alcohol intake
- ○ Decreased sleep
- ○ Medication change
- ○ Increased stress
- ○ Weather
- ○ Amount of light
- ○ Strong smells
- ○ Loud sounds
- ○ Hormone change
- ○ Pressure on head
- ○ Vitamin/mineral deficiency
- ○ Change in exercise
- ○ Travel
- ○ Other:_____

Feelings afterward?

- ○ Feel normal
- ○ Depressed
- ○ Very happy
- ○ Fatigued
- ○ Decreased concentration
- ○ Other:_____

Additional details of headache:

Date:_____ Time:_____

How long did the headache last:_____

How severe is the pain? (Circle a number)

1   2   3   4   5   6   7   8   9   10

Warning signs (hours to days prior)?

- Mood change
- Decreased concentration
- Visual disturbance
- Physical symptoms
- Fatigue
- Sensitivity to light, sounds, or smells
- Neck discomfort
- Difficult speaking/reading
- Nausea
- Change in bowel habits
- Food cravings/thirst
- Yawning
- Other:_____

Headache symptoms?

- Pain on one side
- Pain on both sides
- Throbbing pain
- Constant pain
- Sensitive to light
- Sensitive to sound
- Worse with movement
- Nausea/vomiting
- Nasal congestion
- Feeling cold or warm
- Sensitive to smell/touch
- Neck pain
- Visual or other physical symptoms
- Other:_____

Potential triggers?

- Diet change
- Change in water/caffeine/alcohol intake
- Decreased sleep
- Medication change
- Increased stress
- Weather
- Amount of light
- Strong smells
- Loud sounds
- Hormone change
- Pressure on head
- Vitamin/mineral deficiency
- Change in exercise
- Travel
- Other:_____

Feelings afterward?

- Feel normal
- Depressed
- Very happy
- Fatigued
- Decreased concentration
- Other:_____

Additional details of headache:

Date:_____ Time:_____

How long did the headache last:_____

How severe is the pain? (Circle a number)

1   2   3   4   5   6   7   8   9   10

Warning signs (hours to days prior)?

- Mood change
- Decreased concentration
- Visual disturbance
- Physical symptoms
- Fatigue
- Sensitivity to light, sounds, or smells
- Neck discomfort
- Difficult speaking/reading
- Nausea
- Change in bowel habits
- Food cravings/thirst
- Yawning
- Other:_____

Headache symptoms?

- Pain on one side
- Pain on both sides
- Throbbing pain
- Constant pain
- Sensitive to light
- Sensitive to sound
- Worse with movement
- Nausea/vomiting
- Nasal congestion
- Feeling cold or warm
- Sensitive to smell/touch
- Neck pain
- Visual or other physical symptoms
- Other:_____

Potential triggers?

- Diet change
- Change in water/caffeine/alcohol intake
- Decreased sleep
- Medication change
- Increased stress
- Weather
- Amount of light
- Strong smells
- Loud sounds
- Hormone change
- Pressure on head
- Vitamin/mineral deficiency
- Change in exercise
- Travel
- Other:_____

Feelings afterward?

- Feel normal
- Depressed
- Very happy
- Fatigued
- Decreased concentration
- Other:_____

Additional details of headache:

Date:_____ Time:_____

How long did the headache last:_____

How severe is the pain? (Circle a number)

1 2 3 4 5 6 7 8 9 10

Warning signs (hours to days prior)?

- Mood change
- Decreased concentration
- Visual disturbance
- Physical symptoms
- Fatigue
- Sensitivity to light, sounds, or smells
- Neck discomfort
- Difficult speaking/reading
- Nausea
- Change in bowel habits
- Food cravings/thirst
- Yawning
- Other:_____

Headache symptoms?

- Pain on one side
- Pain on both sides
- Throbbing pain
- Constant pain
- Sensitive to light
- Sensitive to sound
- Worse with movement
- Nausea/vomiting
- Nasal congestion
- Feeling cold or warm
- Sensitive to smell/touch
- Neck pain
- Visual or other physical symptoms
- Other:_____

Potential triggers?

- Diet change
- Change in water/caffeine/alcohol intake
- Decreased sleep
- Medication change
- Increased stress
- Weather
- Amount of light
- Strong smells
- Loud sounds
- Hormone change
- Pressure on head
- Vitamin/mineral deficiency
- Change in exercise
- Travel
- Other:_____

Feelings afterward?

- Feel normal
- Depressed
- Very happy
- Fatigued
- Decreased concentration
- Other:_____

Additional details of headache:

Date:_____ Time:_____

How long did the headache last:_____

How severe is the pain? (Circle a number)

1   2   3   4   5   6   7   8   9   10

Warning signs (hours to days prior)?

○ Mood change
○ Decreased concentration
○ Visual disturbance
○ Physical symptoms
○ Fatigue
○ Sensitivity to light, sounds, or smells
○ Neck discomfort
○ Difficult speaking/reading
○ Nausea
○ Change in bowel habits
○ Food cravings/thirst
○ Yawning
○ Other:_____

Headache symptoms?

○ Pain on one side
○ Pain on both sides
○ Throbbing pain
○ Constant pain
○ Sensitive to light
○ Sensitive to sound
○ Worse with movement
○ Nausea/vomiting
○ Nasal congestion
○ Feeling cold or warm
○ Sensitive to smell/touch
○ Neck pain
○ Visual or other physical symptoms
○ Other:_____

Potential triggers?

○ Diet change
○ Change in water/caffeine/alcohol intake
○ Decreased sleep
○ Medication change
○ Increased stress
○ Weather
○ Amount of light
○ Strong smells
○ Loud sounds
○ Hormone change
○ Pressure on head
○ Vitamin/mineral deficiency
○ Change in exercise
○ Travel
○ Other:_____

Feelings afterward?

○ Feel normal
○ Depressed
○ Very happy
○ Fatigued
○ Decreased concentration
○ Other:_____

Additional details of headache:

Date:_____ Time:_____

How long did the headache last:_____

How severe is the pain? (Circle a number)

1 2 3 4 5 6 7 8 9 10

Warning signs (hours to days prior)?

- Mood change
- Decreased concentration
- Visual disturbance
- Physical symptoms
- Fatigue
- Sensitivity to light, sounds, or smells
- Neck discomfort
- Difficult speaking/reading
- Nausea
- Change in bowel habits
- Food cravings/thirst
- Yawning
- Other:_____

Headache symptoms?

- Pain on one side
- Pain on both sides
- Throbbing pain
- Constant pain
- Sensitive to light
- Sensitive to sound
- Worse with movement
- Nausea/vomiting
- Nasal congestion
- Feeling cold or warm
- Sensitive to smell/touch
- Neck pain
- Visual or other physical symptoms
- Other:_____

Potential triggers?

- Diet change
- Change in water/caffeine/alcohol intake
- Decreased sleep
- Medication change
- Increased stress
- Weather
- Amount of light
- Strong smells
- Loud sounds
- Hormone change
- Pressure on head
- Vitamin/mineral deficiency
- Change in exercise
- Travel
- Other:_____

Feelings afterward?

- Feel normal
- Depressed
- Very happy
- Fatigued
- Decreased concentration
- Other:_____

Additional details of headache:

Date:_____ Time:_____

How long did the headache last:_____

How severe is the pain? (Circle a number)

1   2   3   4   5   6   7   8   9   10

Warning signs (hours to days prior)?

- Mood change
- Decreased concentration
- Visual disturbance
- Physical symptoms
- Fatigue
- Sensitivity to light, sounds, or smells
- Neck discomfort
- Difficult speaking/reading
- Nausea
- Change in bowel habits
- Food cravings/thirst
- Yawning
- Other:_____

Headache symptoms?

- Pain on one side
- Pain on both sides
- Throbbing pain
- Constant pain
- Sensitive to light
- Sensitive to sound
- Worse with movement
- Nausea/vomiting
- Nasal congestion
- Feeling cold or warm
- Sensitive to smell/touch
- Neck pain
- Visual or other physical symptoms
- Other:_____

Potential triggers?

- Diet change
- Change in water/caffeine/alcohol intake
- Decreased sleep
- Medication change
- Increased stress
- Weather
- Amount of light
- Strong smells
- Loud sounds
- Hormone change
- Pressure on head
- Vitamin/mineral deficiency
- Change in exercise
- Travel
- Other:_____

Feelings afterward?

- Feel normal
- Depressed
- Very happy
- Fatigued
- Decreased concentration
- Other:_____

Additional details of headache:

Date:_____ Time:_____

How long did the headache last:_____

How severe is the pain? (Circle a number)

1   2   3   4   5   6   7   8   9   10

**Warning signs
(hours to days prior)?**

- Mood change
- Decreased concentration
- Visual disturbance
- Physical symptoms
- Fatigue
- Sensitivity to light, sounds, or smells
- Neck discomfort
- Difficult speaking/reading
- Nausea
- Change in bowel habits
- Food cravings/thirst
- Yawning
- Other:_____

Headache symptoms?

- Pain on one side
- Pain on both sides
- Throbbing pain
- Constant pain
- Sensitive to light
- Sensitive to sound
- Worse with movement
- Nausea/vomiting
- Nasal congestion
- Feeling cold or warm
- Sensitive to smell/touch
- Neck pain
- Visual or other physical symptoms
- Other:_____

Potential triggers?

- Diet change
- Change in water/caffeine/alcohol intake
- Decreased sleep
- Medication change
- Increased stress
- Weather
- Amount of light
- Strong smells
- Loud sounds
- Hormone change
- Pressure on head
- Vitamin/mineral deficiency
- Change in exercise
- Travel
- Other:_____

Feelings afterward?

- Feel normal
- Depressed
- Very happy
- Fatigued
- Decreased concentration
- Other:_____

Additional details of headache:

Date:_____ Time:_____

How long did the headache last:_____

How severe is the pain? (Circle a number)

1 2 3 4 5 6 7 8 9 10

Warning signs (hours to days prior)?

- ○ Mood change
- ○ Decreased concentration
- ○ Visual disturbance
- ○ Physical symptoms
- ○ Fatigue
- ○ Sensitivity to light, sounds, or smells
- ○ Neck discomfort
- ○ Difficult speaking/reading
- ○ Nausea
- ○ Change in bowel habits
- ○ Food cravings/thirst
- ○ Yawning
- ○ Other:_____

Headache symptoms?

- ○ Pain on one side
- ○ Pain on both sides
- ○ Throbbing pain
- ○ Constant pain
- ○ Sensitive to light
- ○ Sensitive to sound
- ○ Worse with movement
- ○ Nausea/vomiting
- ○ Nasal congestion
- ○ Feeling cold or warm
- ○ Sensitive to smell/touch
- ○ Neck pain
- ○ Visual or other physical symptoms
- ○ Other:_____

Potential triggers?

- ○ Diet change
- ○ Change in water/caffeine/alcohol intake
- ○ Decreased sleep
- ○ Medication change
- ○ Increased stress
- ○ Weather
- ○ Amount of light
- ○ Strong smells
- ○ Loud sounds
- ○ Hormone change
- ○ Pressure on head
- ○ Vitamin/mineral deficiency
- ○ Change in exercise
- ○ Travel
- ○ Other:_____

Feelings afterward?

- ○ Feel normal
- ○ Depressed
- ○ Very happy
- ○ Fatigued
- ○ Decreased concentration
- ○ Other:_____

Additional details of headache:

Date:_____ Time:_____

How long did the headache last:_____

How severe is the pain? (Circle a number)

1   2   3   4   5   6   7   8   9   10

Warning signs (hours to days prior)?

- Mood change
- Decreased concentration
- Visual disturbance
- Physical symptoms
- Fatigue
- Sensitivity to light, sounds, or smells
- Neck discomfort
- Difficult speaking/reading
- Nausea
- Change in bowel habits
- Food cravings/thirst
- Yawning
- Other:_____

Headache symptoms?

- Pain on one side
- Pain on both sides
- Throbbing pain
- Constant pain
- Sensitive to light
- Sensitive to sound
- Worse with movement
- Nausea/vomiting
- Nasal congestion
- Feeling cold or warm
- Sensitive to smell/touch
- Neck pain
- Visual or other physical symptoms
- Other:_____

Potential triggers?

- Diet change
- Change in water/caffeine/alcohol intake
- Decreased sleep
- Medication change
- Increased stress
- Weather
- Amount of light
- Strong smells
- Loud sounds
- Hormone change
- Pressure on head
- Vitamin/mineral deficiency
- Change in exercise
- Travel
- Other:_____

Feelings afterward?

- Feel normal
- Depressed
- Very happy
- Fatigued
- Decreased concentration
- Other:_____

Additional details of headache:

Date:_____ Time:_____

How long did the headache last:_____

How severe is the pain? (Circle a number)

1 2 3 4 5 6 7 8 9 10

Warning signs (hours to days prior)?

- ◯ Mood change
- ◯ Decreased concentration
- ◯ Visual disturbance
- ◯ Physical symptoms
- ◯ Fatigue
- ◯ Sensitivity to light, sounds, or smells
- ◯ Neck discomfort
- ◯ Difficult speaking/reading
- ◯ Nausea
- ◯ Change in bowel habits
- ◯ Food cravings/thirst
- ◯ Yawning
- ◯ Other:_____

Headache symptoms?

- ◯ Pain on one side
- ◯ Pain on both sides
- ◯ Throbbing pain
- ◯ Constant pain
- ◯ Sensitive to light
- ◯ Sensitive to sound
- ◯ Worse with movement
- ◯ Nausea/vomiting
- ◯ Nasal congestion
- ◯ Feeling cold or warm
- ◯ Sensitive to smell/touch
- ◯ Neck pain
- ◯ Visual or other physical symptoms
- ◯ Other:_____

Potential triggers?

- ◯ Diet change
- ◯ Change in water/caffeine/alcohol intake
- ◯ Decreased sleep
- ◯ Medication change
- ◯ Increased stress
- ◯ Weather
- ◯ Amount of light
- ◯ Strong smells
- ◯ Loud sounds
- ◯ Hormone change
- ◯ Pressure on head
- ◯ Vitamin/mineral deficiency
- ◯ Change in exercise
- ◯ Travel
- ◯ Other:_____

Feelings afterward?

- ◯ Feel normal
- ◯ Depressed
- ◯ Very happy
- ◯ Fatigued
- ◯ Decreased concentration
- ◯ Other:_____

Additional details of headache:

Date:_____ Time:_____

How long did the headache last:_____

How severe is the pain? (Circle a number)

1 2 3 4 5 6 7 8 9 10

Warning signs (hours to days prior)?

- Mood change
- Decreased concentration
- Visual disturbance
- Physical symptoms
- Fatigue
- Sensitivity to light, sounds, or smells
- Neck discomfort
- Difficult speaking/reading
- Nausea
- Change in bowel habits
- Food cravings/thirst
- Yawning
- Other:_____

Headache symptoms?

- Pain on one side
- Pain on both sides
- Throbbing pain
- Constant pain
- Sensitive to light
- Sensitive to sound
- Worse with movement
- Nausea/vomiting
- Nasal congestion
- Feeling cold or warm
- Sensitive to smell/touch
- Neck pain
- Visual or other physical symptoms
- Other:_____

Potential triggers?

- Diet change
- Change in water/caffeine/alcohol intake
- Decreased sleep
- Medication change
- Increased stress
- Weather
- Amount of light
- Strong smells
- Loud sounds
- Hormone change
- Pressure on head
- Vitamin/mineral deficiency
- Change in exercise
- Travel
- Other:_____

Feelings afterward?

- Feel normal
- Depressed
- Very happy
- Fatigued
- Decreased concentration
- Other:_____

Additional details of headache:

Date:_____ Time:_____

How long did the headache last:_____

How severe is the pain? (Circle a number)

1 2 3 4 5 6 7 8 9 10

Warning signs (hours to days prior)?

- ◯ Mood change
- ◯ Decreased concentration
- ◯ Visual disturbance
- ◯ Physical symptoms
- ◯ Fatigue
- ◯ Sensitivity to light, sounds, or smells
- ◯ Neck discomfort
- ◯ Difficult speaking/reading
- ◯ Nausea
- ◯ Change in bowel habits
- ◯ Food cravings/thirst
- ◯ Yawning
- ◯ Other:_____

Headache symptoms?

- ◯ Pain on one side
- ◯ Pain on both sides
- ◯ Throbbing pain
- ◯ Constant pain
- ◯ Sensitive to light
- ◯ Sensitive to sound
- ◯ Worse with movement
- ◯ Nausea/vomiting
- ◯ Nasal congestion
- ◯ Feeling cold or warm
- ◯ Sensitive to smell/touch
- ◯ Neck pain
- ◯ Visual or other physical symptoms
- ◯ Other:_____

Potential triggers?

- ◯ Diet change
- ◯ Change in water/caffeine/alcohol intake
- ◯ Decreased sleep
- ◯ Medication change
- ◯ Increased stress
- ◯ Weather
- ◯ Amount of light
- ◯ Strong smells
- ◯ Loud sounds
- ◯ Hormone change
- ◯ Pressure on head
- ◯ Vitamin/mineral deficiency
- ◯ Change in exercise
- ◯ Travel
- ◯ Other:_____

Feelings afterward?

- ◯ Feel normal
- ◯ Depressed
- ◯ Very happy
- ◯ Fatigued
- ◯ Decreased concentration
- ◯ Other:_____

Additional details of headache:

Date:_____ Time:_____

How long did the headache last:_____

How severe is the pain? (Circle a number)

1   2   3   4   5   6   7   8   9   10

Warning signs (hours to days prior)?

- Mood change
- Decreased concentration
- Visual disturbance
- Physical symptoms
- Fatigue
- Sensitivity to light, sounds, or smells
- Neck discomfort
- Difficult speaking/reading
- Nausea
- Change in bowel habits
- Food cravings/thirst
- Yawning
- Other:_____

Headache symptoms?

- Pain on one side
- Pain on both sides
- Throbbing pain
- Constant pain
- Sensitive to light
- Sensitive to sound
- Worse with movement
- Nausea/vomiting
- Nasal congestion
- Feeling cold or warm
- Sensitive to smell/touch
- Neck pain
- Visual or other physical symptoms
- Other:_____

Potential triggers?

- Diet change
- Change in water/caffeine/alcohol intake
- Decreased sleep
- Medication change
- Increased stress
- Weather
- Amount of light
- Strong smells
- Loud sounds
- Hormone change
- Pressure on head
- Vitamin/mineral deficiency
- Change in exercise
- Travel
- Other:_____

Feelings afterward?

- Feel normal
- Depressed
- Very happy
- Fatigued
- Decreased concentration
- Other:_____

Additional details of headache:

Date:_____ Time:_____

How long did the headache last:_____

How severe is the pain? (Circle a number)

1   2   3   4   5   6   7   8   9   10

Warning signs (hours to days prior)?

- ○ Mood change
- ○ Decreased concentration
- ○ Visual disturbance
- ○ Physical symptoms
- ○ Fatigue
- ○ Sensitivity to light, sounds, or smells
- ○ Neck discomfort
- ○ Difficult speaking/reading
- ○ Nausea
- ○ Change in bowel habits
- ○ Food cravings/thirst
- ○ Yawning
- ○ Other:_____

Headache symptoms?

- ○ Pain on one side
- ○ Pain on both sides
- ○ Throbbing pain
- ○ Constant pain
- ○ Sensitive to light
- ○ Sensitive to sound
- ○ Worse with movement
- ○ Nausea/vomiting
- ○ Nasal congestion
- ○ Feeling cold or warm
- ○ Sensitive to smell/touch
- ○ Neck pain
- ○ Visual or other physical symptoms
- ○ Other:_____

Potential triggers?

- ○ Diet change
- ○ Change in water/caffeine/alcohol intake
- ○ Decreased sleep
- ○ Medication change
- ○ Increased stress
- ○ Weather
- ○ Amount of light
- ○ Strong smells
- ○ Loud sounds
- ○ Hormone change
- ○ Pressure on head
- ○ Vitamin/mineral deficiency
- ○ Change in exercise
- ○ Travel
- ○ Other:_____

Feelings afterward?

- ○ Feel normal
- ○ Depressed
- ○ Very happy
- ○ Fatigued
- ○ Decreased concentration
- ○ Other:_____

Additional details of headache:

Date:_____ Time:_____

How long did the headache last:_____

How severe is the pain? (Circle a number)

1 2 3 4 5 6 7 8 9 10

Warning signs (hours to days prior)?

- Mood change
- Decreased concentration
- Visual disturbance
- Physical symptoms
- Fatigue
- Sensitivity to light, sounds, or smells
- Neck discomfort
- Difficult speaking/reading
- Nausea
- Change in bowel habits
- Food cravings/thirst
- Yawning
- Other:_____

Headache symptoms?

- Pain on one side
- Pain on both sides
- Throbbing pain
- Constant pain
- Sensitive to light
- Sensitive to sound
- Worse with movement
- Nausea/vomiting
- Nasal congestion
- Feeling cold or warm
- Sensitive to smell/touch
- Neck pain
- Visual or other physical symptoms
- Other:_____

Potential triggers?

- Diet change
- Change in water/caffeine/alcohol intake
- Decreased sleep
- Medication change
- Increased stress
- Weather
- Amount of light
- Strong smells
- Loud sounds
- Hormone change
- Pressure on head
- Vitamin/mineral deficiency
- Change in exercise
- Travel
- Other:_____

Feelings afterward?

- Feel normal
- Depressed
- Very happy
- Fatigued
- Decreased concentration
- Other:_____

Additional details of headache:

Date:_____ Time:_____

How long did the headache last:_____

How severe is the pain? (Circle a number)

1 2 3 4 5 6 7 8 9 10

Warning signs (hours to days prior)?

○ Mood change
○ Decreased concentration
○ Visual disturbance
○ Physical symptoms
○ Fatigue
○ Sensitivity to light, sounds, or smells
○ Neck discomfort
○ Difficult speaking/reading
○ Nausea
○ Change in bowel habits
○ Food cravings/thirst
○ Yawning
○ Other:_____

Headache symptoms?

○ Pain on one side
○ Pain on both sides
○ Throbbing pain
○ Constant pain
○ Sensitive to light
○ Sensitive to sound
○ Worse with movement
○ Nausea/vomiting
○ Nasal congestion
○ Feeling cold or warm
○ Sensitive to smell/touch
○ Neck pain
○ Visual or other physical symptoms
○ Other:_____

Potential triggers?

○ Diet change
○ Change in water/caffeine/alcohol intake
○ Decreased sleep
○ Medication change
○ Increased stress
○ Weather
○ Amount of light
○ Strong smells
○ Loud sounds
○ Hormone change
○ Pressure on head
○ Vitamin/mineral deficiency
○ Change in exercise
○ Travel
○ Other:_____

Feelings afterward?

○ Feel normal
○ Depressed
○ Very happy
○ Fatigued
○ Decreased concentration
○ Other:_____

Additional details of headache:

Date:_____ Time:_____

How long did the headache last:_____

How severe is the pain? (Circle a number)

1 2 3 4 5 6 7 8 9 10

Warning signs (hours to days prior)?

- Mood change
- Decreased concentration
- Visual disturbance
- Physical symptoms
- Fatigue
- Sensitivity to light, sounds, or smells
- Neck discomfort
- Difficult speaking/reading
- Nausea
- Change in bowel habits
- Food cravings/thirst
- Yawning
- Other:_____

Headache symptoms?

- Pain on one side
- Pain on both sides
- Throbbing pain
- Constant pain
- Sensitive to light
- Sensitive to sound
- Worse with movement
- Nausea/vomiting
- Nasal congestion
- Feeling cold or warm
- Sensitive to smell/touch
- Neck pain
- Visual or other physical symptoms
- Other:_____

Potential triggers?

- Diet change
- Change in water/caffeine/alcohol intake
- Decreased sleep
- Medication change
- Increased stress
- Weather
- Amount of light
- Strong smells
- Loud sounds
- Hormone change
- Pressure on head
- Vitamin/mineral deficiency
- Change in exercise
- Travel
- Other:_____

Feelings afterward?

- Feel normal
- Depressed
- Very happy
- Fatigued
- Decreased concentration
- Other:_____

Additional details of headache:

Date:_____ Time:_____

How long did the headache last:_____

How severe is the pain? (Circle a number)

1   2   3   4   5   6   7   8   9   10

Warning signs (hours to days prior)?

- ○ Mood change
- ○ Decreased concentration
- ○ Visual disturbance
- ○ Physical symptoms
- ○ Fatigue
- ○ Sensitivity to light, sounds, or smells
- ○ Neck discomfort
- ○ Difficult speaking/reading
- ○ Nausea
- ○ Change in bowel habits
- ○ Food cravings/thirst
- ○ Yawning
- ○ Other:_____

Headache symptoms?

- ○ Pain on one side
- ○ Pain on both sides
- ○ Throbbing pain
- ○ Constant pain
- ○ Sensitive to light
- ○ Sensitive to sound
- ○ Worse with movement
- ○ Nausea/vomiting
- ○ Nasal congestion
- ○ Feeling cold or warm
- ○ Sensitive to smell/touch
- ○ Neck pain
- ○ Visual or other physical symptoms
- ○ Other:_____

Potential triggers?

- ○ Diet change
- ○ Change in water/caffeine/alcohol intake
- ○ Decreased sleep
- ○ Medication change
- ○ Increased stress
- ○ Weather
- ○ Amount of light
- ○ Strong smells
- ○ Loud sounds
- ○ Hormone change
- ○ Pressure on head
- ○ Vitamin/mineral deficiency
- ○ Change in exercise
- ○ Travel
- ○ Other:_____

Feelings afterward?

- ○ Feel normal
- ○ Depressed
- ○ Very happy
- ○ Fatigued
- ○ Decreased concentration
- ○ Other:_____

Additional details of headache:

Date:_____ Time:_____

How long did the headache last:_____

How severe is the pain? (Circle a number)

1   2   3   4   5   6   7   8   9   10

Warning signs (hours to days prior)?

- Mood change
- Decreased concentration
- Visual disturbance
- Physical symptoms
- Fatigue
- Sensitivity to light, sounds, or smells
- Neck discomfort
- Difficult speaking/reading
- Nausea
- Change in bowel habits
- Food cravings/thirst
- Yawning
- Other:_____

Headache symptoms?

- Pain on one side
- Pain on both sides
- Throbbing pain
- Constant pain
- Sensitive to light
- Sensitive to sound
- Worse with movement
- Nausea/vomiting
- Nasal congestion
- Feeling cold or warm
- Sensitive to smell/touch
- Neck pain
- Visual or other physical symptoms
- Other:_____

Potential triggers?

- Diet change
- Change in water/caffeine/alcohol intake
- Decreased sleep
- Medication change
- Increased stress
- Weather
- Amount of light
- Strong smells
- Loud sounds
- Hormone change
- Pressure on head
- Vitamin/mineral deficiency
- Change in exercise
- Travel
- Other:_____

Feelings afterward?

- Feel normal
- Depressed
- Very happy
- Fatigued
- Decreased concentration
- Other:_____

Additional details of headache:

Date:_____ Time:_____

How long did the headache last:_____

How severe is the pain? (Circle a number)

1   2   3   4   5   6   7   8   9   10

Warning signs (hours to days prior)?

- ○ Mood change
- ○ Decreased concentration
- ○ Visual disturbance
- ○ Physical symptoms
- ○ Fatigue
- ○ Sensitivity to light, sounds, or smells
- ○ Neck discomfort
- ○ Difficult speaking/reading
- ○ Nausea
- ○ Change in bowel habits
- ○ Food cravings/thirst
- ○ Yawning
- ○ Other:_____

Headache symptoms?

- ○ Pain on one side
- ○ Pain on both sides
- ○ Throbbing pain
- ○ Constant pain
- ○ Sensitive to light
- ○ Sensitive to sound
- ○ Worse with movement
- ○ Nausea/vomiting
- ○ Nasal congestion
- ○ Feeling cold or warm
- ○ Sensitive to smell/touch
- ○ Neck pain
- ○ Visual or other physical symptoms
- ○ Other:_____

Potential triggers?

- ○ Diet change
- ○ Change in water/caffeine/alcohol intake
- ○ Decreased sleep
- ○ Medication change
- ○ Increased stress
- ○ Weather
- ○ Amount of light
- ○ Strong smells
- ○ Loud sounds
- ○ Hormone change
- ○ Pressure on head
- ○ Vitamin/mineral deficiency
- ○ Change in exercise
- ○ Travel
- ○ Other:_____

Feelings afterward?

- ○ Feel normal
- ○ Depressed
- ○ Very happy
- ○ Fatigued
- ○ Decreased concentration
- ○ Other:_____

Additional details of headache:

Date:_____ Time:_____

How long did the headache last:_____

How severe is the pain? (Circle a number)

1 2 3 4 5 6 7 8 9 10

Warning signs (hours to days prior)?

Mood change
Decreased concentration
Visual disturbance
Physical symptoms
Fatigue
Sensitivity to light, sounds, or smells
Neck discomfort
Difficult speaking/reading
Nausea
Change in bowel habits
Food cravings/thirst
Yawning
Other:_____

Potential triggers?

Diet change
Change in water/caffeine/alcohol intake
Decreased sleep
Medication change
Increased stress
Weather
Amount of light
Strong smells
Loud sounds
Hormone change
Pressure on head
Vitamin/mineral deficiency
Change in exercise
Travel
Other:_____

Headache symptoms?

Pain on one side
Pain on both sides
Throbbing pain
Constant pain
Sensitive to light
Sensitive to sound
Worse with movement
Nausea/vomiting
Nasal congestion
Feeling cold or warm
Sensitive to smell/touch
Neck pain
Visual or other physical symptoms
Other:_____

Feelings afterward?

Feel normal
Depressed
Very happy
Fatigued
Decreased concentration
Other:_____

Additional details of headache:

Date:_____ Time:_____

How long did the headache last:_____

How severe is the pain? (Circle a number)

1 2 3 4 5 6 7 8 9 10

Warning signs (hours to days prior)?

- ○ Mood change
- ○ Decreased concentration
- ○ Visual disturbance
- ○ Physical symptoms
- ○ Fatigue
- ○ Sensitivity to light, sounds, or smells
- ○ Neck discomfort
- ○ Difficult speaking/reading
- ○ Nausea
- ○ Change in bowel habits
- ○ Food cravings/thirst
- ○ Yawning
- ○ Other:_____

Headache symptoms?

- ○ Pain on one side
- ○ Pain on both sides
- ○ Throbbing pain
- ○ Constant pain
- ○ Sensitive to light
- ○ Sensitive to sound
- ○ Worse with movement
- ○ Nausea/vomiting
- ○ Nasal congestion
- ○ Feeling cold or warm
- ○ Sensitive to smell/touch
- ○ Neck pain
- ○ Visual or other physical symptoms
- ○ Other:_____

Potential triggers?

- ○ Diet change
- ○ Change in water/caffeine/alcohol intake
- ○ Decreased sleep
- ○ Medication change
- ○ Increased stress
- ○ Weather
- ○ Amount of light
- ○ Strong smells
- ○ Loud sounds
- ○ Hormone change
- ○ Pressure on head
- ○ Vitamin/mineral deficiency
- ○ Change in exercise
- ○ Travel
- ○ Other:_____

Feelings afterward?

- ○ Feel normal
- ○ Depressed
- ○ Very happy
- ○ Fatigued
- ○ Decreased concentration
- ○ Other:_____

Additional details of headache:

Date:_____ Time:_____

How long did the headache last:_____

How severe is the pain? (Circle a number)

1   2   3   4   5   6   7   8   9   10

Warning signs (hours to days prior)?

- Mood change
- Decreased concentration
- Visual disturbance
- Physical symptoms
- Fatigue
- Sensitivity to light, sounds, or smells
- Neck discomfort
- Difficult speaking/reading
- Nausea
- Change in bowel habits
- Food cravings/thirst
- Yawning
- Other:_____

Headache symptoms?

- Pain on one side
- Pain on both sides
- Throbbing pain
- Constant pain
- Sensitive to light
- Sensitive to sound
- Worse with movement
- Nausea/vomiting
- Nasal congestion
- Feeling cold or warm
- Sensitive to smell/touch
- Neck pain
- Visual or other physical symptoms
- Other:_____

Potential triggers?

- Diet change
- Change in water/caffeine/alcohol intake
- Decreased sleep
- Medication change
- Increased stress
- Weather
- Amount of light
- Strong smells
- Loud sounds
- Hormone change
- Pressure on head
- Vitamin/mineral deficiency
- Change in exercise
- Travel
- Other:_____

Feelings afterward?

- Feel normal
- Depressed
- Very happy
- Fatigued
- Decreased concentration
- Other:_____

Additional details of headache:

Date:_____ Time:_____

How long did the headache last:_____

How severe is the pain? (Circle a number)

1 2 3 4 5 6 7 8 9 10

Warning signs (hours to days prior)?

- Mood change
- Decreased concentration
- Visual disturbance
- Physical symptoms
- Fatigue
- Sensitivity to light, sounds, or smells
- Neck discomfort
- Difficult speaking/reading
- Nausea
- Change in bowel habits
- Food cravings/thirst
- Yawning
- Other:_____

Headache symptoms?

- Pain on one side
- Pain on both sides
- Throbbing pain
- Constant pain
- Sensitive to light
- Sensitive to sound
- Worse with movement
- Nausea/vomiting
- Nasal congestion
- Feeling cold or warm
- Sensitive to smell/touch
- Neck pain
- Visual or other physical symptoms
- Other:_____

Potential triggers?

- Diet change
- Change in water/caffeine/alcohol intake
- Decreased sleep
- Medication change
- Increased stress
- Weather
- Amount of light
- Strong smells
- Loud sounds
- Hormone change
- Pressure on head
- Vitamin/mineral deficiency
- Change in exercise
- Travel
- Other:_____

Feelings afterward?

- Feel normal
- Depressed
- Very happy
- Fatigued
- Decreased concentration
- Other:_____

Additional details of headache:

Date:_____ Time:_____

How long did the headache last:_____

How severe is the pain? (Circle a number)

1   2   3   4   5   6   7   8   9   10

Warning signs (hours to days prior)?

- Mood change
- Decreased concentration
- Visual disturbance
- Physical symptoms
- Fatigue
- Sensitivity to light, sounds, or smells
- Neck discomfort
- Difficult speaking/reading
- Nausea
- Change in bowel habits
- Food cravings/thirst
- Yawning
- Other:_____

Headache symptoms?

- Pain on one side
- Pain on both sides
- Throbbing pain
- Constant pain
- Sensitive to light
- Sensitive to sound
- Worse with movement
- Nausea/vomiting
- Nasal congestion
- Feeling cold or warm
- Sensitive to smell/touch
- Neck pain
- Visual or other physical symptoms
- Other:_____

Potential triggers?

- Diet change
- Change in water/caffeine/alcohol intake
- Decreased sleep
- Medication change
- Increased stress
- Weather
- Amount of light
- Strong smells
- Loud sounds
- Hormone change
- Pressure on head
- Vitamin/mineral deficiency
- Change in exercise
- Travel
- Other:_____

Feelings afterward?

- Feel normal
- Depressed
- Very happy
- Fatigued
- Decreased concentration
- Other:_____

Additional details of headache:

Date:_____ Time:_____

How long did the headache last:_____

How severe is the pain? (Circle a number)

1   2   3   4   5   6   7   8   9   10

Warning signs (hours to days prior)?

- ○ Mood change
- ○ Decreased concentration
- ○ Visual disturbance
- ○ Physical symptoms
- ○ Fatigue
- ○ Sensitivity to light, sounds, or smells
- ○ Neck discomfort
- ○ Difficult speaking/reading
- ○ Nausea
- ○ Change in bowel habits
- ○ Food cravings/thirst
- ○ Yawning
- ○ Other:_____

Headache symptoms?

- ○ Pain on one side
- ○ Pain on both sides
- ○ Throbbing pain
- ○ Constant pain
- ○ Sensitive to light
- ○ Sensitive to sound
- ○ Worse with movement
- ○ Nausea/vomiting
- ○ Nasal congestion
- ○ Feeling cold or warm
- ○ Sensitive to smell/touch
- ○ Neck pain
- ○ Visual or other physical symptoms
- ○ Other:_____

Potential triggers?

- ○ Diet change
- ○ Change in water/caffeine/alcohol intake
- ○ Decreased sleep
- ○ Medication change
- ○ Increased stress
- ○ Weather
- ○ Amount of light
- ○ Strong smells
- ○ Loud sounds
- ○ Hormone change
- ○ Pressure on head
- ○ Vitamin/mineral deficiency
- ○ Change in exercise
- ○ Travel
- ○ Other:_____

Feelings afterward?

- ○ Feel normal
- ○ Depressed
- ○ Very happy
- ○ Fatigued
- ○ Decreased concentration
- ○ Other:_____

Additional details of headache:

Date:_____ Time:_____

How long did the headache last:_____

How severe is the pain? (Circle a number)

1　2　3　4　5　6　7　8　9　10

Warning signs (hours to days prior)?

- Mood change
- Decreased concentration
- Visual disturbance
- Physical symptoms
- Fatigue
- Sensitivity to light, sounds, or smells
- Neck discomfort
- Difficult speaking/reading
- Nausea
- Change in bowel habits
- Food cravings/thirst
- Yawning
- Other:_____

Headache symptoms?

- Pain on one side
- Pain on both sides
- Throbbing pain
- Constant pain
- Sensitive to light
- Sensitive to sound
- Worse with movement
- Nausea/vomiting
- Nasal congestion
- Feeling cold or warm
- Sensitive to smell/touch
- Neck pain
- Visual or other physical symptoms
- Other:_____

Potential triggers?

- Diet change
- Change in water/caffeine/alcohol intake
- Decreased sleep
- Medication change
- Increased stress
- Weather
- Amount of light
- Strong smells
- Loud sounds
- Hormone change
- Pressure on head
- Vitamin/mineral deficiency
- Change in exercise
- Travel
- Other:_____

Feelings afterward?

- Feel normal
- Depressed
- Very happy
- Fatigued
- Decreased concentration
- Other:_____

Additional details of headache:

Date:_____ Time:_____

How long did the headache last:_____

How severe is the pain? (Circle a number)

1 2 3 4 5 6 7 8 9 10

Warning signs (hours to days prior)?

- Mood change
- Decreased concentration
- Visual disturbance
- Physical symptoms
- Fatigue
- Sensitivity to light, sounds, or smells
- Neck discomfort
- Difficult speaking/reading
- Nausea
- Change in bowel habits
- Food cravings/thirst
- Yawning
- Other:_____

Headache symptoms?

- Pain on one side
- Pain on both sides
- Throbbing pain
- Constant pain
- Sensitive to light
- Sensitive to sound
- Worse with movement
- Nausea/vomiting
- Nasal congestion
- Feeling cold or warm
- Sensitive to smell/touch
- Neck pain
- Visual or other physical symptoms
- Other:_____

Potential triggers?

- Diet change
- Change in water/caffeine/alcohol intake
- Decreased sleep
- Medication change
- Increased stress
- Weather
- Amount of light
- Strong smells
- Loud sounds
- Hormone change
- Pressure on head
- Vitamin/mineral deficiency
- Change in exercise
- Travel
- Other:_____

Feelings afterward?

- Feel normal
- Depressed
- Very happy
- Fatigued
- Decreased concentration
- Other:_____

Additional details of headache:

Date:_____ Time:_____

How long did the headache last:_____

How severe is the pain? (Circle a number)

1 2 3 4 5 6 7 8 9 10

Warning signs (hours to days prior)?

- Mood change
- Decreased concentration
- Visual disturbance
- Physical symptoms
- Fatigue
- Sensitivity to light, sounds, or smells
- Neck discomfort
- Difficult speaking/reading
- Nausea
- Change in bowel habits
- Food cravings/thirst
- Yawning
- Other:_____

Headache symptoms?

- Pain on one side
- Pain on both sides
- Throbbing pain
- Constant pain
- Sensitive to light
- Sensitive to sound
- Worse with movement
- Nausea/vomiting
- Nasal congestion
- Feeling cold or warm
- Sensitive to smell/touch
- Neck pain
- Visual or other physical symptoms
- Other:_____

Potential triggers?

- Diet change
- Change in water/caffeine/alcohol intake
- Decreased sleep
- Medication change
- Increased stress
- Weather
- Amount of light
- Strong smells
- Loud sounds
- Hormone change
- Pressure on head
- Vitamin/mineral deficiency
- Change in exercise
- Travel
- Other:_____

Feelings afterward?

- Feel normal
- Depressed
- Very happy
- Fatigued
- Decreased concentration
- Other:_____

Additional details of headache:

Date:_____ Time:_____

How long did the headache last:_____

How severe is the pain? (Circle a number)

1   2   3   4   5   6   7   8   9   10

Warning signs (hours to days prior)?

- Mood change
- Decreased concentration
- Visual disturbance
- Physical symptoms
- Fatigue
- Sensitivity to light, sounds, or smells
- Neck discomfort
- Difficult speaking/reading
- Nausea
- Change in bowel habits
- Food cravings/thirst
- Yawning
- Other:_____

Headache symptoms?

- Pain on one side
- Pain on both sides
- Throbbing pain
- Constant pain
- Sensitive to light
- Sensitive to sound
- Worse with movement
- Nausea/vomiting
- Nasal congestion
- Feeling cold or warm
- Sensitive to smell/touch
- Neck pain
- Visual or other physical symptoms
- Other:_____

Potential triggers?

- Diet change
- Change in water/caffeine/alcohol intake
- Decreased sleep
- Medication change
- Increased stress
- Weather
- Amount of light
- Strong smells
- Loud sounds
- Hormone change
- Pressure on head
- Vitamin/mineral deficiency
- Change in exercise
- Travel
- Other:_____

Feelings afterward?

- Feel normal
- Depressed
- Very happy
- Fatigued
- Decreased concentration
- Other:_____

Additional details of headache:

Date:_____ Time:_____

How long did the headache last:_____

How severe is the pain? (Circle a number)

1   2   3   4   5   6   7   8   9   10

**Warning signs
(hours to days prior)?**
- Mood change
- Decreased concentration
- Visual disturbance
- Physical symptoms
- Fatigue
- Sensitivity to light, sounds, or smells
- Neck discomfort
- Difficult speaking/reading
- Nausea
- Change in bowel habits
- Food cravings/thirst
- Yawning
- Other:_____

Headache symptoms?
- Pain on one side
- Pain on both sides
- Throbbing pain
- Constant pain
- Sensitive to light
- Sensitive to sound
- Worse with movement
- Nausea/vomiting
- Nasal congestion
- Feeling cold or warm
- Sensitive to smell/touch
- Neck pain
- Visual or other physical symptoms
- Other:_____

Potential triggers?
- Diet change
- Change in water/caffeine/alcohol intake
- Decreased sleep
- Medication change
- Increased stress
- Weather
- Amount of light
- Strong smells
- Loud sounds
- Hormone change
- Pressure on head
- Vitamin/mineral deficiency
- Change in exercise
- Travel
- Other:_____

Feelings afterward?
- Feel normal
- Depressed
- Very happy
- Fatigued
- Decreased concentration
- Other:_____

Additional details of headache:

Date:_____ Time:_____

How long did the headache last:_____

How severe is the pain? (Circle a number)

1   2   3   4   5   6   7   8   9   10

Warning signs (hours to days prior)?

- ○ Mood change
- ○ Decreased concentration
- ○ Visual disturbance
- ○ Physical symptoms
- ○ Fatigue
- ○ Sensitivity to light, sounds, or smells
- ○ Neck discomfort
- ○ Difficult speaking/reading
- ○ Nausea
- ○ Change in bowel habits
- ○ Food cravings/thirst
- ○ Yawning
- ○ Other:_____

Headache symptoms?

- ○ Pain on one side
- ○ Pain on both sides
- ○ Throbbing pain
- ○ Constant pain
- ○ Sensitive to light
- ○ Sensitive to sound
- ○ Worse with movement
- ○ Nausea/vomiting
- ○ Nasal congestion
- ○ Feeling cold or warm
- ○ Sensitive to smell/touch
- ○ Neck pain
- ○ Visual or other physical symptoms
- ○ Other:_____

Potential triggers?

- ○ Diet change
- ○ Change in water/caffeine/alcohol intake
- ○ Decreased sleep
- ○ Medication change
- ○ Increased stress
- ○ Weather
- ○ Amount of light
- ○ Strong smells
- ○ Loud sounds
- ○ Hormone change
- ○ Pressure on head
- ○ Vitamin/mineral deficiency
- ○ Change in exercise
- ○ Travel
- ○ Other:_____

Feelings afterward?

- ○ Feel normal
- ○ Depressed
- ○ Very happy
- ○ Fatigued
- ○ Decreased concentration
- ○ Other:_____

Additional details of headache:

Date:_____ Time:_____

How long did the headache last:_____

How severe is the pain? (Circle a number)

1 2 3 4 5 6 7 8 9 10

Warning signs (hours to days prior)?

- Mood change
- Decreased concentration
- Visual disturbance
- Physical symptoms
- Fatigue
- Sensitivity to light, sounds, or smells
- Neck discomfort
- Difficult speaking/reading
- Nausea
- Change in bowel habits
- Food cravings/thirst
- Yawning
- Other:_____

Headache symptoms?

- Pain on one side
- Pain on both sides
- Throbbing pain
- Constant pain
- Sensitive to light
- Sensitive to sound
- Worse with movement
- Nausea/vomiting
- Nasal congestion
- Feeling cold or warm
- Sensitive to smell/touch
- Neck pain
- Visual or other physical symptoms
- Other:_____

Potential triggers?

- Diet change
- Change in water/caffeine/alcohol intake
- Decreased sleep
- Medication change
- Increased stress
- Weather
- Amount of light
- Strong smells
- Loud sounds
- Hormone change
- Pressure on head
- Vitamin/mineral deficiency
- Change in exercise
- Travel
- Other:_____

Feelings afterward?

- Feel normal
- Depressed
- Very happy
- Fatigued
- Decreased concentration
- Other:_____

Additional details of headache:

Date:_____ Time:_____

How long did the headache last:_____

How severe is the pain? (Circle a number)

1   2   3   4   5   6   7   8   9   10

Warning signs (hours to days prior)?

- ◯ Mood change
- ◯ Decreased concentration
- ◯ Visual disturbance
- ◯ Physical symptoms
- ◯ Fatigue
- ◯ Sensitivity to light, sounds, or smells
- ◯ Neck discomfort
- ◯ Difficult speaking/reading
- ◯ Nausea
- ◯ Change in bowel habits
- ◯ Food cravings/thirst
- ◯ Yawning
- ◯ Other:_____

Headache symptoms?

- ◯ Pain on one side
- ◯ Pain on both sides
- ◯ Throbbing pain
- ◯ Constant pain
- ◯ Sensitive to light
- ◯ Sensitive to sound
- ◯ Worse with movement
- ◯ Nausea/vomiting
- ◯ Nasal congestion
- ◯ Feeling cold or warm
- ◯ Sensitive to smell/touch
- ◯ Neck pain
- ◯ Visual or other physical symptoms
- ◯ Other:_____

Potential triggers?

- ◯ Diet change
- ◯ Change in water/caffeine/alcohol intake
- ◯ Decreased sleep
- ◯ Medication change
- ◯ Increased stress
- ◯ Weather
- ◯ Amount of light
- ◯ Strong smells
- ◯ Loud sounds
- ◯ Hormone change
- ◯ Pressure on head
- ◯ Vitamin/mineral deficiency
- ◯ Change in exercise
- ◯ Travel
- ◯ Other:_____

Feelings afterward?

- ◯ Feel normal
- ◯ Depressed
- ◯ Very happy
- ◯ Fatigued
- ◯ Decreased concentration
- ◯ Other:_____

Additional details of headache:

Date:_____ Time:_____

How long did the headache last:_____

How severe is the pain? (Circle a number)

1　2　3　4　5　6　7　8　9　10

Warning signs (hours to days prior)?

- Mood change
- Decreased concentration
- Visual disturbance
- Physical symptoms
- Fatigue
- Sensitivity to light, sounds, or smells
- Neck discomfort
- Difficult speaking/reading
- Nausea
- Change in bowel habits
- Food cravings/thirst
- Yawning
- Other:_____

Headache symptoms?

- Pain on one side
- Pain on both sides
- Throbbing pain
- Constant pain
- Sensitive to light
- Sensitive to sound
- Worse with movement
- Nausea/vomiting
- Nasal congestion
- Feeling cold or warm
- Sensitive to smell/touch
- Neck pain
- Visual or other physical symptoms
- Other:_____

Potential triggers?

- Diet change
- Change in water/caffeine/alcohol intake
- Decreased sleep
- Medication change
- Increased stress
- Weather
- Amount of light
- Strong smells
- Loud sounds
- Hormone change
- Pressure on head
- Vitamin/mineral deficiency
- Change in exercise
- Travel
- Other:_____

Feelings afterward?

- Feel normal
- Depressed
- Very happy
- Fatigued
- Decreased concentration
- Other:_____

Additional details of headache:

Date:_____ Time:_____

How long did the headache last:_____

How severe is the pain? (Circle a number)

1   2   3   4   5   6   7   8   9   10

Warning signs (hours to days prior)?

- Mood change
- Decreased concentration
- Visual disturbance
- Physical symptoms
- Fatigue
- Sensitivity to light, sounds, or smells
- Neck discomfort
- Difficult speaking/reading
- Nausea
- Change in bowel habits
- Food cravings/thirst
- Yawning
- Other:_____

Headache symptoms?

- Pain on one side
- Pain on both sides
- Throbbing pain
- Constant pain
- Sensitive to light
- Sensitive to sound
- Worse with movement
- Nausea/vomiting
- Nasal congestion
- Feeling cold or warm
- Sensitive to smell/touch
- Neck pain
- Visual or other physical symptoms
- Other:_____

Potential triggers?

- Diet change
- Change in water/caffeine/alcohol intake
- Decreased sleep
- Medication change
- Increased stress
- Weather
- Amount of light
- Strong smells
- Loud sounds
- Hormone change
- Pressure on head
- Vitamin/mineral deficiency
- Change in exercise
- Travel
- Other:_____

Feelings afterward?

- Feel normal
- Depressed
- Very happy
- Fatigued
- Decreased concentration
- Other:_____

Additional details of headache:

Date:_____ Time:_____

How long did the headache last:_____

How severe is the pain? (Circle a number)

1   2   3   4   5   6   7   8   9   10

Warning signs (hours to days prior)?

- Mood change
- Decreased concentration
- Visual disturbance
- Physical symptoms
- Fatigue
- Sensitivity to light, sounds, or smells
- Neck discomfort
- Difficult speaking/reading
- Nausea
- Change in bowel habits
- Food cravings/thirst
- Yawning
- Other:_____

Headache symptoms?

- Pain on one side
- Pain on both sides
- Throbbing pain
- Constant pain
- Sensitive to light
- Sensitive to sound
- Worse with movement
- Nausea/vomiting
- Nasal congestion
- Feeling cold or warm
- Sensitive to smell/touch
- Neck pain
- Visual or other physical symptoms
- Other:_____

Potential triggers?

- Diet change
- Change in water/caffeine/alcohol intake
- Decreased sleep
- Medication change
- Increased stress
- Weather
- Amount of light
- Strong smells
- Loud sounds
- Hormone change
- Pressure on head
- Vitamin/mineral deficiency
- Change in exercise
- Travel
- Other:_____

Feelings afterward?

- Feel normal
- Depressed
- Very happy
- Fatigued
- Decreased concentration
- Other:_____

Additional details of headache:

Date:_____ Time:_____

How long did the headache last:_____

How severe is the pain? (Circle a number)

1   2   3   4   5   6   7   8   9   10

Warning signs (hours to days prior)?

- Mood change
- Decreased concentration
- Visual disturbance
- Physical symptoms
- Fatigue
- Sensitivity to light, sounds, or smells
- Neck discomfort
- Difficult speaking/reading
- Nausea
- Change in bowel habits
- Food cravings/thirst
- Yawning
- Other:_____

Headache symptoms?

- Pain on one side
- Pain on both sides
- Throbbing pain
- Constant pain
- Sensitive to light
- Sensitive to sound
- Worse with movement
- Nausea/vomiting
- Nasal congestion
- Feeling cold or warm
- Sensitive to smell/touch
- Neck pain
- Visual or other physical symptoms
- Other:_____

Potential triggers?

- Diet change
- Change in water/caffeine/alcohol intake
- Decreased sleep
- Medication change
- Increased stress
- Weather
- Amount of light
- Strong smells
- Loud sounds
- Hormone change
- Pressure on head
- Vitamin/mineral deficiency
- Change in exercise
- Travel
- Other:_____

Feelings afterward?

- Feel normal
- Depressed
- Very happy
- Fatigued
- Decreased concentration
- Other:_____

Additional details of headache:

Date:_____ Time:_____

How long did the headache last:_____

How severe is the pain? (Circle a number)

1   2   3   4   5   6   7   8   9   10

Warning signs (hours to days prior)?

- Mood change
- Decreased concentration
- Visual disturbance
- Physical symptoms
- Fatigue
- Sensitivity to light, sounds, or smells
- Neck discomfort
- Difficult speaking/reading
- Nausea
- Change in bowel habits
- Food cravings/thirst
- Yawning
- Other:_____

Headache symptoms?

- Pain on one side
- Pain on both sides
- Throbbing pain
- Constant pain
- Sensitive to light
- Sensitive to sound
- Worse with movement
- Nausea/vomiting
- Nasal congestion
- Feeling cold or warm
- Sensitive to smell/touch
- Neck pain
- Visual or other physical symptoms
- Other:_____

Potential triggers?

- Diet change
- Change in water/caffeine/alcohol intake
- Decreased sleep
- Medication change
- Increased stress
- Weather
- Amount of light
- Strong smells
- Loud sounds
- Hormone change
- Pressure on head
- Vitamin/mineral deficiency
- Change in exercise
- Travel
- Other:_____

Feelings afterward?

- Feel normal
- Depressed
- Very happy
- Fatigued
- Decreased concentration
- Other:_____

Additional details of headache:

Date:_____ Time:_____

How long did the headache last:_____

How severe is the pain? (Circle a number)

1 2 3 4 5 6 7 8 9 10

Warning signs (hours to days prior)?

- ○ Mood change
- ○ Decreased concentration
- ○ Visual disturbance
- ○ Physical symptoms
- ○ Fatigue
- ○ Sensitivity to light, sounds, or smells
- ○ Neck discomfort
- ○ Difficult speaking/reading
- ○ Nausea
- ○ Change in bowel habits
- ○ Food cravings/thirst
- ○ Yawning
- ○ Other:_____

Headache symptoms?

- ○ Pain on one side
- ○ Pain on both sides
- ○ Throbbing pain
- ○ Constant pain
- ○ Sensitive to light
- ○ Sensitive to sound
- ○ Worse with movement
- ○ Nausea/vomiting
- ○ Nasal congestion
- ○ Feeling cold or warm
- ○ Sensitive to smell/touch
- ○ Neck pain
- ○ Visual or other physical symptoms
- ○ Other:_____

Potential triggers?

- ○ Diet change
- ○ Change in water/caffeine/alcohol intake
- ○ Decreased sleep
- ○ Medication change
- ○ Increased stress
- ○ Weather
- ○ Amount of light
- ○ Strong smells
- ○ Loud sounds
- ○ Hormone change
- ○ Pressure on head
- ○ Vitamin/mineral deficiency
- ○ Change in exercise
- ○ Travel
- ○ Other:_____

Feelings afterward?

- ○ Feel normal
- ○ Depressed
- ○ Very happy
- ○ Fatigued
- ○ Decreased concentration
- ○ Other:_____

Additional details of headache:

Date:_____ Time:_____

How long did the headache last:_____

How severe is the pain? (Circle a number)

1　2　3　4　5　6　7　8　9　10

Warning signs (hours to days prior)?

- Mood change
- Decreased concentration
- Visual disturbance
- Physical symptoms
- Fatigue
- Sensitivity to light, sounds, or smells
- Neck discomfort
- Difficult speaking/reading
- Nausea
- Change in bowel habits
- Food cravings/thirst
- Yawning
- Other:_____

Headache symptoms?

- Pain on one side
- Pain on both sides
- Throbbing pain
- Constant pain
- Sensitive to light
- Sensitive to sound
- Worse with movement
- Nausea/vomiting
- Nasal congestion
- Feeling cold or warm
- Sensitive to smell/touch
- Neck pain
- Visual or other physical symptoms
- Other:_____

Potential triggers?

- Diet change
- Change in water/caffeine/alcohol intake
- Decreased sleep
- Medication change
- Increased stress
- Weather
- Amount of light
- Strong smells
- Loud sounds
- Hormone change
- Pressure on head
- Vitamin/mineral deficiency
- Change in exercise
- Travel
- Other:_____

Feelings afterward?

- Feel normal
- Depressed
- Very happy
- Fatigued
- Decreased concentration
- Other:_____

Additional details of headache:

Date:_____ Time:_____

How long did the headache last:_____

How severe is the pain? (Circle a number)

1   2   3   4   5   6   7   8   9   10

Warning signs (hours to days prior)?

- Mood change
- Decreased concentration
- Visual disturbance
- Physical symptoms
- Fatigue
- Sensitivity to light, sounds, or smells
- Neck discomfort
- Difficult speaking/reading
- Nausea
- Change in bowel habits
- Food cravings/thirst
- Yawning
- Other:_____

Headache symptoms?

- Pain on one side
- Pain on both sides
- Throbbing pain
- Constant pain
- Sensitive to light
- Sensitive to sound
- Worse with movement
- Nausea/vomiting
- Nasal congestion
- Feeling cold or warm
- Sensitive to smell/touch
- Neck pain
- Visual or other physical symptoms
- Other:_____

Potential triggers?

- Diet change
- Change in water/caffeine/alcohol intake
- Decreased sleep
- Medication change
- Increased stress
- Weather
- Amount of light
- Strong smells
- Loud sounds
- Hormone change
- Pressure on head
- Vitamin/mineral deficiency
- Change in exercise
- Travel
- Other:_____

Feelings afterward?

- Feel normal
- Depressed
- Very happy
- Fatigued
- Decreased concentration
- Other:_____

Additional details of headache:

Date:_____ Time:_____

How long did the headache last:_____

How severe is the pain? (Circle a number)

1   2   3   4   5   6   7   8   9   10

Warning signs (hours to days prior)?

- Mood change
- Decreased concentration
- Visual disturbance
- Physical symptoms
- Fatigue
- Sensitivity to light, sounds, or smells
- Neck discomfort
- Difficult speaking/reading
- Nausea
- Change in bowel habits
- Food cravings/thirst
- Yawning
- Other:_____

Headache symptoms?

- Pain on one side
- Pain on both sides
- Throbbing pain
- Constant pain
- Sensitive to light
- Sensitive to sound
- Worse with movement
- Nausea/vomiting
- Nasal congestion
- Feeling cold or warm
- Sensitive to smell/touch
- Neck pain
- Visual or other physical symptoms
- Other:_____

Potential triggers?

- Diet change
- Change in water/caffeine/alcohol intake
- Decreased sleep
- Medication change
- Increased stress
- Weather
- Amount of light
- Strong smells
- Loud sounds
- Hormone change
- Pressure on head
- Vitamin/mineral deficiency
- Change in exercise
- Travel
- Other:_____

Feelings afterward?

- Feel normal
- Depressed
- Very happy
- Fatigued
- Decreased concentration
- Other:_____

Additional details of headache:

Date:_____ Time:_____

How long did the headache last:_____

How severe is the pain? (Circle a number)

1 2 3 4 5 6 7 8 9 10

Warning signs (hours to days prior)?

○ Mood change
○ Decreased concentration
○ Visual disturbance
○ Physical symptoms
○ Fatigue
○ Sensitivity to light, sounds, or smells
○ Neck discomfort
○ Difficult speaking/reading
○ Nausea
○ Change in bowel habits
○ Food cravings/thirst
○ Yawning
○ Other:_____

Headache symptoms?

○ Pain on one side
○ Pain on both sides
○ Throbbing pain
○ Constant pain
○ Sensitive to light
○ Sensitive to sound
○ Worse with movement
○ Nausea/vomiting
○ Nasal congestion
○ Feeling cold or warm
○ Sensitive to smell/touch
○ Neck pain
○ Visual or other physical symptoms
○ Other:_____

Potential triggers?

○ Diet change
○ Change in water/caffeine/alcohol intake
○ Decreased sleep
○ Medication change
○ Increased stress
○ Weather
○ Amount of light
○ Strong smells
○ Loud sounds
○ Hormone change
○ Pressure on head
○ Vitamin/mineral deficiency
○ Change in exercise
○ Travel
○ Other:_____

Feelings afterward?

○ Feel normal
○ Depressed
○ Very happy
○ Fatigued
○ Decreased concentration
○ Other:_____

Additional details of headache:

Date:_____ Time:_____

How long did the headache last:_____

How severe is the pain? (Circle a number)

1 2 3 4 5 6 7 8 9 10

Warning signs (hours to days prior)?

- Mood change
- Decreased concentration
- Visual disturbance
- Physical symptoms
- Fatigue
- Sensitivity to light, sounds, or smells
- Neck discomfort
- Difficult speaking/reading
- Nausea
- Change in bowel habits
- Food cravings/thirst
- Yawning
- Other:_____

Headache symptoms?

- Pain on one side
- Pain on both sides
- Throbbing pain
- Constant pain
- Sensitive to light
- Sensitive to sound
- Worse with movement
- Nausea/vomiting
- Nasal congestion
- Feeling cold or warm
- Sensitive to smell/touch
- Neck pain
- Visual or other physical symptoms
- Other:_____

Potential triggers?

- Diet change
- Change in water/caffeine/alcohol intake
- Decreased sleep
- Medication change
- Increased stress
- Weather
- Amount of light
- Strong smells
- Loud sounds
- Hormone change
- Pressure on head
- Vitamin/mineral deficiency
- Change in exercise
- Travel
- Other:_____

Feelings afterward?

- Feel normal
- Depressed
- Very happy
- Fatigued
- Decreased concentration
- Other:_____

Additional details of headache:

Date:_____ Time:_____

How long did the headache last:_____

How severe is the pain? (Circle a number)

1   2   3   4   5   6   7   8   9   10

Warning signs (hours to days prior)?
○ Mood change
○ Decreased concentration
○ Visual disturbance
○ Physical symptoms
○ Fatigue
○ Sensitivity to light, sounds, or smells
○ Neck discomfort
○ Difficult speaking/reading
○ Nausea
○ Change in bowel habits
○ Food cravings/thirst
○ Yawning
○ Other:_____

Headache symptoms?
○ Pain on one side
○ Pain on both sides
○ Throbbing pain
○ Constant pain
○ Sensitive to light
○ Sensitive to sound
○ Worse with movement
○ Nausea/vomiting
○ Nasal congestion
○ Feeling cold or warm
○ Sensitive to smell/touch
○ Neck pain
○ Visual or other physical symptoms
○ Other:_____

Potential triggers?
○ Diet change
○ Change in water/caffeine/alcohol intake
○ Decreased sleep
○ Medication change
○ Increased stress
○ Weather
○ Amount of light
○ Strong smells
○ Loud sounds
○ Hormone change
○ Pressure on head
○ Vitamin/mineral deficiency
○ Change in exercise
○ Travel
○ Other:_____

Feelings afterward?
○ Feel normal
○ Depressed
○ Very happy
○ Fatigued
○ Decreased concentration
○ Other:_____

Additional details of headache:

Date:_____ Time:_____

How long did the headache last:_____

How severe is the pain? (Circle a number)

1 2 3 4 5 6 7 8 9 10

Warning signs (hours to days prior)?

- Mood change
- Decreased concentration
- Visual disturbance
- Physical symptoms
- Fatigue
- Sensitivity to light, sounds, or smells
- Neck discomfort
- Difficult speaking/reading
- Nausea
- Change in bowel habits
- Food cravings/thirst
- Yawning
- Other:_____

Headache symptoms?

- Pain on one side
- Pain on both sides
- Throbbing pain
- Constant pain
- Sensitive to light
- Sensitive to sound
- Worse with movement
- Nausea/vomiting
- Nasal congestion
- Feeling cold or warm
- Sensitive to smell/touch
- Neck pain
- Visual or other physical symptoms
- Other:_____

Potential triggers?

- Diet change
- Change in water/caffeine/alcohol intake
- Decreased sleep
- Medication change
- Increased stress
- Weather
- Amount of light
- Strong smells
- Loud sounds
- Hormone change
- Pressure on head
- Vitamin/mineral deficiency
- Change in exercise
- Travel
- Other:_____

Feelings afterward?

- Feel normal
- Depressed
- Very happy
- Fatigued
- Decreased concentration
- Other:_____

Additional details of headache:

Date:_____ Time:_____

How long did the headache last:_____

How severe is the pain? (Circle a number)

1   2   3   4   5   6   7   8   9   10

Warning signs (hours to days prior)?

- ○ Mood change
- ○ Decreased concentration
- ○ Visual disturbance
- ○ Physical symptoms
- ○ Fatigue
- ○ Sensitivity to light, sounds, or smells
- ○ Neck discomfort
- ○ Difficult speaking/reading
- ○ Nausea
- ○ Change in bowel habits
- ○ Food cravings/thirst
- ○ Yawning
- ○ Other:_____

Headache symptoms?

- ○ Pain on one side
- ○ Pain on both sides
- ○ Throbbing pain
- ○ Constant pain
- ○ Sensitive to light
- ○ Sensitive to sound
- ○ Worse with movement
- ○ Nausea/vomiting
- ○ Nasal congestion
- ○ Feeling cold or warm
- ○ Sensitive to smell/touch
- ○ Neck pain
- ○ Visual or other physical symptoms
- ○ Other:_____

Potential triggers?

- ○ Diet change
- ○ Change in water/caffeine/alcohol intake
- ○ Decreased sleep
- ○ Medication change
- ○ Increased stress
- ○ Weather
- ○ Amount of light
- ○ Strong smells
- ○ Loud sounds
- ○ Hormone change
- ○ Pressure on head
- ○ Vitamin/mineral deficiency
- ○ Change in exercise
- ○ Travel
- ○ Other:_____

Feelings afterward?

- ○ Feel normal
- ○ Depressed
- ○ Very happy
- ○ Fatigued
- ○ Decreased concentration
- ○ Other:_____

Additional details of headache:

Date:_____ Time:_____

How long did the headache last:_____

How severe is the pain? (Circle a number)

1   2   3   4   5   6   7   8   9   10

Warning signs (hours to days prior)?

- Mood change
- Decreased concentration
- Visual disturbance
- Physical symptoms
- Fatigue
- Sensitivity to light, sounds, or smells
- Neck discomfort
- Difficult speaking/reading
- Nausea
- Change in bowel habits
- Food cravings/thirst
- Yawning
- Other:_____

Headache symptoms?

- Pain on one side
- Pain on both sides
- Throbbing pain
- Constant pain
- Sensitive to light
- Sensitive to sound
- Worse with movement
- Nausea/vomiting
- Nasal congestion
- Feeling cold or warm
- Sensitive to smell/touch
- Neck pain
- Visual or other physical symptoms
- Other:_____

Potential triggers?

- Diet change
- Change in water/caffeine/alcohol intake
- Decreased sleep
- Medication change
- Increased stress
- Weather
- Amount of light
- Strong smells
- Loud sounds
- Hormone change
- Pressure on head
- Vitamin/mineral deficiency
- Change in exercise
- Travel
- Other:_____

Feelings afterward?

- Feel normal
- Depressed
- Very happy
- Fatigued
- Decreased concentration
- Other:_____

Additional details of headache:

Date:_____ Time:_____

How long did the headache last:_____

How severe is the pain? (Circle a number)

1 2 3 4 5 6 7 8 9 10

Warning signs (hours to days prior)?

- ○ Mood change
- ○ Decreased concentration
- ○ Visual disturbance
- ○ Physical symptoms
- ○ Fatigue
- ○ Sensitivity to light, sounds, or smells
- ○ Neck discomfort
- ○ Difficult speaking/reading
- ○ Nausea
- ○ Change in bowel habits
- ○ Food cravings/thirst
- ○ Yawning
- ○ Other:_____

Headache symptoms?

- ○ Pain on one side
- ○ Pain on both sides
- ○ Throbbing pain
- ○ Constant pain
- ○ Sensitive to light
- ○ Sensitive to sound
- ○ Worse with movement
- ○ Nausea/vomiting
- ○ Nasal congestion
- ○ Feeling cold or warm
- ○ Sensitive to smell/touch
- ○ Neck pain
- ○ Visual or other physical symptoms
- ○ Other:_____

Potential triggers?

- ○ Diet change
- ○ Change in water/caffeine/alcohol intake
- ○ Decreased sleep
- ○ Medication change
- ○ Increased stress
- ○ Weather
- ○ Amount of light
- ○ Strong smells
- ○ Loud sounds
- ○ Hormone change
- ○ Pressure on head
- ○ Vitamin/mineral deficiency
- ○ Change in exercise
- ○ Travel
- ○ Other:_____

Feelings afterward?

- ○ Feel normal
- ○ Depressed
- ○ Very happy
- ○ Fatigued
- ○ Decreased concentration
- ○ Other:_____

Additional details of headache:

Date:_____ Time:_____

How long did the headache last:_____

How severe is the pain? (Circle a number)

1   2   3   4   5   6   7   8   9   10

Warning signs (hours to days prior)?

- Mood change
- Decreased concentration
- Visual disturbance
- Physical symptoms
- Fatigue
- Sensitivity to light, sounds, or smells
- Neck discomfort
- Difficult speaking/reading
- Nausea
- Change in bowel habits
- Food cravings/thirst
- Yawning
- Other:_____

Headache symptoms?

- Pain on one side
- Pain on both sides
- Throbbing pain
- Constant pain
- Sensitive to light
- Sensitive to sound
- Worse with movement
- Nausea/vomiting
- Nasal congestion
- Feeling cold or warm
- Sensitive to smell/touch
- Neck pain
- Visual or other physical symptoms
- Other:_____

Potential triggers?

- Diet change
- Change in water/caffeine/alcohol intake
- Decreased sleep
- Medication change
- Increased stress
- Weather
- Amount of light
- Strong smells
- Loud sounds
- Hormone change
- Pressure on head
- Vitamin/mineral deficiency
- Change in exercise
- Travel
- Other:_____

Feelings afterward?

- Feel normal
- Depressed
- Very happy
- Fatigued
- Decreased concentration
- Other:_____

Additional details of headache:

Date:_____ Time:_____

How long did the headache last:_____

How severe is the pain? (Circle a number)

1   2   3   4   5   6   7   8   9   10

Warning signs (hours to days prior)?

○ Mood change
○ Decreased concentration
○ Visual disturbance
○ Physical symptoms
○ Fatigue
○ Sensitivity to light, sounds, or smells
○ Neck discomfort
○ Difficult speaking/reading
○ Nausea
○ Change in bowel habits
○ Food cravings/thirst
○ Yawning
○ Other:_____

Headache symptoms?

○ Pain on one side
○ Pain on both sides
○ Throbbing pain
○ Constant pain
○ Sensitive to light
○ Sensitive to sound
○ Worse with movement
○ Nausea/vomiting
○ Nasal congestion
○ Feeling cold or warm
○ Sensitive to smell/touch
○ Neck pain
○ Visual or other physical symptoms
○ Other:_____

Potential triggers?

○ Diet change
○ Change in water/caffeine/alcohol intake
○ Decreased sleep
○ Medication change
○ Increased stress
○ Weather
○ Amount of light
○ Strong smells
○ Loud sounds
○ Hormone change
○ Pressure on head
○ Vitamin/mineral deficiency
○ Change in exercise
○ Travel
○ Other:_____

Feelings afterward?

○ Feel normal
○ Depressed
○ Very happy
○ Fatigued
○ Decreased concentration
○ Other:_____

Additional details of headache:

Date:_____ Time:_____

How long did the headache last:_____

How severe is the pain? (Circle a number)

1   2   3   4   5   6   7   8   9   10

Warning signs (hours to days prior)?

- ○ Mood change
- ○ Decreased concentration
- ○ Visual disturbance
- ○ Physical symptoms
- ○ Fatigue
- ○ Sensitivity to light, sounds, or smells
- ○ Neck discomfort
- ○ Difficult speaking/reading
- ○ Nausea
- ○ Change in bowel habits
- ○ Food cravings/thirst
- ○ Yawning
- ○ Other:_____

Headache symptoms?

- ○ Pain on one side
- ○ Pain on both sides
- ○ Throbbing pain
- ○ Constant pain
- ○ Sensitive to light
- ○ Sensitive to sound
- ○ Worse with movement
- ○ Nausea/vomiting
- ○ Nasal congestion
- ○ Feeling cold or warm
- ○ Sensitive to smell/touch
- ○ Neck pain
- ○ Visual or other physical symptoms
- ○ Other:_____

Potential triggers?

- ○ Diet change
- ○ Change in water/caffeine/alcohol intake
- ○ Decreased sleep
- ○ Medication change
- ○ Increased stress
- ○ Weather
- ○ Amount of light
- ○ Strong smells
- ○ Loud sounds
- ○ Hormone change
- ○ Pressure on head
- ○ Vitamin/mineral deficiency
- ○ Change in exercise
- ○ Travel
- ○ Other:_____

Feelings afterward?

- ○ Feel normal
- ○ Depressed
- ○ Very happy
- ○ Fatigued
- ○ Decreased concentration
- ○ Other:_____

Additional details of headache:

Date:_____ Time:_____

How long did the headache last:_____

How severe is the pain? (Circle a number)

1   2   3   4   5   6   7   8   9   10

Warning signs (hours to days prior)?

- ○ Mood change
- ○ Decreased concentration
- ○ Visual disturbance
- ○ Physical symptoms
- ○ Fatigue
- ○ Sensitivity to light, sounds, or smells
- ○ Neck discomfort
- ○ Difficult speaking/reading
- ○ Nausea
- ○ Change in bowel habits
- ○ Food cravings/thirst
- ○ Yawning
- ○ Other:_____

Headache symptoms?

- ○ Pain on one side
- ○ Pain on both sides
- ○ Throbbing pain
- ○ Constant pain
- ○ Sensitive to light
- ○ Sensitive to sound
- ○ Worse with movement
- ○ Nausea/vomiting
- ○ Nasal congestion
- ○ Feeling cold or warm
- ○ Sensitive to smell/touch
- ○ Neck pain
- ○ Visual or other physical symptoms
- ○ Other:_____

Potential triggers?

- ○ Diet change
- ○ Change in water/caffeine/alcohol intake
- ○ Decreased sleep
- ○ Medication change
- ○ Increased stress
- ○ Weather
- ○ Amount of light
- ○ Strong smells
- ○ Loud sounds
- ○ Hormone change
- ○ Pressure on head
- ○ Vitamin/mineral deficiency
- ○ Change in exercise
- ○ Travel
- ○ Other:_____

Feelings afterward?

- ○ Feel normal
- ○ Depressed
- ○ Very happy
- ○ Fatigued
- ○ Decreased concentration
- ○ Other:_____

Additional details of headache:

Date:_____ Time:_____

How long did the headache last:_____

How severe is the pain? (Circle a number)

1   2   3   4   5   6   7   8   9   10

Warning signs (hours to days prior)?

- Mood change
- Decreased concentration
- Visual disturbance
- Physical symptoms
- Fatigue
- Sensitivity to light, sounds, or smells
- Neck discomfort
- Difficult speaking/reading
- Nausea
- Change in bowel habits
- Food cravings/thirst
- Yawning
- Other:_____

Headache symptoms?

- Pain on one side
- Pain on both sides
- Throbbing pain
- Constant pain
- Sensitive to light
- Sensitive to sound
- Worse with movement
- Nausea/vomiting
- Nasal congestion
- Feeling cold or warm
- Sensitive to smell/touch
- Neck pain
- Visual or other physical symptoms
- Other:_____

Potential triggers?

- Diet change
- Change in water/caffeine/alcohol intake
- Decreased sleep
- Medication change
- Increased stress
- Weather
- Amount of light
- Strong smells
- Loud sounds
- Hormone change
- Pressure on head
- Vitamin/mineral deficiency
- Change in exercise
- Travel
- Other:_____

Feelings afterward?

- Feel normal
- Depressed
- Very happy
- Fatigued
- Decreased concentration
- Other:_____

Additional details of headache:

Date:_____ Time:_____

How long did the headache last:_____

How severe is the pain? (Circle a number)

1   2   3   4   5   6   7   8   9   10

Warning signs (hours to days prior)?

- ○ Mood change
- ○ Decreased concentration
- ○ Visual disturbance
- ○ Physical symptoms
- ○ Fatigue
- ○ Sensitivity to light, sounds, or smells
- ○ Neck discomfort
- ○ Difficult speaking/reading
- ○ Nausea
- ○ Change in bowel habits
- ○ Food cravings/thirst
- ○ Yawning
- ○ Other:_____

Headache symptoms?

- ○ Pain on one side
- ○ Pain on both sides
- ○ Throbbing pain
- ○ Constant pain
- ○ Sensitive to light
- ○ Sensitive to sound
- ○ Worse with movement
- ○ Nausea/vomiting
- ○ Nasal congestion
- ○ Feeling cold or warm
- ○ Sensitive to smell/touch
- ○ Neck pain
- ○ Visual or other physical symptoms
- ○ Other:_____

Potential triggers?

- ○ Diet change
- ○ Change in water/caffeine/alcohol intake
- ○ Decreased sleep
- ○ Medication change
- ○ Increased stress
- ○ Weather
- ○ Amount of light
- ○ Strong smells
- ○ Loud sounds
- ○ Hormone change
- ○ Pressure on head
- ○ Vitamin/mineral deficiency
- ○ Change in exercise
- ○ Travel
- ○ Other:_____

Feelings afterward?

- ○ Feel normal
- ○ Depressed
- ○ Very happy
- ○ Fatigued
- ○ Decreased concentration
- ○ Other:_____

Additional details of headache:

Date:_____ Time:_____

How long did the headache last:_____

How severe is the pain? (Circle a number)

1   2   3   4   5   6   7   8   9   10

Warning signs (hours to days prior)?

- Mood change
- Decreased concentration
- Visual disturbance
- Physical symptoms
- Fatigue
- Sensitivity to light, sounds, or smells
- Neck discomfort
- Difficult speaking/reading
- Nausea
- Change in bowel habits
- Food cravings/thirst
- Yawning
- Other:_____

Headache symptoms?

- Pain on one side
- Pain on both sides
- Throbbing pain
- Constant pain
- Sensitive to light
- Sensitive to sound
- Worse with movement
- Nausea/vomiting
- Nasal congestion
- Feeling cold or warm
- Sensitive to smell/touch
- Neck pain
- Visual or other physical symptoms
- Other:_____

Potential triggers?

- Diet change
- Change in water/caffeine/alcohol intake
- Decreased sleep
- Medication change
- Increased stress
- Weather
- Amount of light
- Strong smells
- Loud sounds
- Hormone change
- Pressure on head
- Vitamin/mineral deficiency
- Change in exercise
- Travel
- Other:_____

Feelings afterward?

- Feel normal
- Depressed
- Very happy
- Fatigued
- Decreased concentration
- Other:_____

Additional details of headache:

Date:_____ Time:_____

How long did the headache last:_____

How severe is the pain? (Circle a number)

1 2 3 4 5 6 7 8 9 10

Warning signs (hours to days prior)?

○ Mood change
○ Decreased concentration
○ Visual disturbance
○ Physical symptoms
○ Fatigue
○ Sensitivity to light, sounds, or smells
○ Neck discomfort
○ Difficult speaking/reading
○ Nausea
○ Change in bowel habits
○ Food cravings/thirst
○ Yawning
○ Other:_____

Headache symptoms?

○ Pain on one side
○ Pain on both sides
○ Throbbing pain
○ Constant pain
○ Sensitive to light
○ Sensitive to sound
○ Worse with movement
○ Nausea/vomiting
○ Nasal congestion
○ Feeling cold or warm
○ Sensitive to smell/touch
○ Neck pain
○ Visual or other physical symptoms
○ Other:_____

Potential triggers?

○ Diet change
○ Change in water/caffeine/alcohol intake
○ Decreased sleep
○ Medication change
○ Increased stress
○ Weather
○ Amount of light
○ Strong smells
○ Loud sounds
○ Hormone change
○ Pressure on head
○ Vitamin/mineral deficiency
○ Change in exercise
○ Travel
○ Other:_____

Feelings afterward?

○ Feel normal
○ Depressed
○ Very happy
○ Fatigued
○ Decreased concentration
○ Other:_____

Additional details of headache:

Date:_____ Time:_____

How long did the headache last:_____

How severe is the pain? (Circle a number)

1   2   3   4   5   6   7   8   9   10

Warning signs (hours to days prior)?

- ○ Mood change
- ○ Decreased concentration
- ○ Visual disturbance
- ○ Physical symptoms
- ○ Fatigue
- ○ Sensitivity to light, sounds, or smells
- ○ Neck discomfort
- ○ Difficult speaking/reading
- ○ Nausea
- ○ Change in bowel habits
- ○ Food cravings/thirst
- ○ Yawning
- ○ Other:_____

Headache symptoms?

- ○ Pain on one side
- ○ Pain on both sides
- ○ Throbbing pain
- ○ Constant pain
- ○ Sensitive to light
- ○ Sensitive to sound
- ○ Worse with movement
- ○ Nausea/vomiting
- ○ Nasal congestion
- ○ Feeling cold or warm
- ○ Sensitive to smell/touch
- ○ Neck pain
- ○ Visual or other physical symptoms
- ○ Other:_____

Potential triggers?

- ○ Diet change
- ○ Change in water/caffeine/alcohol intake
- ○ Decreased sleep
- ○ Medication change
- ○ Increased stress
- ○ Weather
- ○ Amount of light
- ○ Strong smells
- ○ Loud sounds
- ○ Hormone change
- ○ Pressure on head
- ○ Vitamin/mineral deficiency
- ○ Change in exercise
- ○ Travel
- ○ Other:_____

Feelings afterward?

- ○ Feel normal
- ○ Depressed
- ○ Very happy
- ○ Fatigued
- ○ Decreased concentration
- ○ Other:_____

Additional details of headache:

Date:_____ Time:_____

How long did the headache last:_____
How severe is the pain? (Circle a number)

1   2   3   4   5   6   7   8   9   10

Warning signs (hours to days prior)?
- ○ Mood change
- ○ Decreased concentration
- ○ Visual disturbance
- ○ Physical symptoms
- ○ Fatigue
- ○ Sensitivity to light, sounds, or smells
- ○ Neck discomfort
- ○ Difficult speaking/reading
- ○ Nausea
- ○ Change in bowel habits
- ○ Food cravings/thirst
- ○ Yawning
- ○ Other:_____

Headache symptoms?
- ○ Pain on one side
- ○ Pain on both sides
- ○ Throbbing pain
- ○ Constant pain
- ○ Sensitive to light
- ○ Sensitive to sound
- ○ Worse with movement
- ○ Nausea/vomiting
- ○ Nasal congestion
- ○ Feeling cold or warm
- ○ Sensitive to smell/touch
- ○ Neck pain
- ○ Visual or other physical symptoms
- ○ Other:_____

Potential triggers?
- ○ Diet change
- ○ Change in water/caffeine/alcohol intake
- ○ Decreased sleep
- ○ Medication change
- ○ Increased stress
- ○ Weather
- ○ Amount of light
- ○ Strong smells
- ○ Loud sounds
- ○ Hormone change
- ○ Pressure on head
- ○ Vitamin/mineral deficiency
- ○ Change in exercise
- ○ Travel
- ○ Other:_____

Feelings afterward?
- ○ Feel normal
- ○ Depressed
- ○ Very happy
- ○ Fatigued
- ○ Decreased concentration
- ○ Other:_____

Additional details of headache:

Date:_____ Time:_____

How long did the headache last:_____

How severe is the pain? (Circle a number)

1   2   3   4   5   6   7   8   9   10

Warning signs (hours to days prior)?

- Mood change
- Decreased concentration
- Visual disturbance
- Physical symptoms
- Fatigue
- Sensitivity to light, sounds, or smells
- Neck discomfort
- Difficult speaking/reading
- Nausea
- Change in bowel habits
- Food cravings/thirst
- Yawning
- Other:_____

Headache symptoms?

- Pain on one side
- Pain on both sides
- Throbbing pain
- Constant pain
- Sensitive to light
- Sensitive to sound
- Worse with movement
- Nausea/vomiting
- Nasal congestion
- Feeling cold or warm
- Sensitive to smell/touch
- Neck pain
- Visual or other physical symptoms
- Other:_____

Potential triggers?

- Diet change
- Change in water/caffeine/alcohol intake
- Decreased sleep
- Medication change
- Increased stress
- Weather
- Amount of light
- Strong smells
- Loud sounds
- Hormone change
- Pressure on head
- Vitamin/mineral deficiency
- Change in exercise
- Travel
- Other:_____

Feelings afterward?

- Feel normal
- Depressed
- Very happy
- Fatigued
- Decreased concentration
- Other:_____

Additional details of headache:

Date:_____ Time:_____

How long did the headache last:_____

How severe is the pain? (Circle a number)

1   2   3   4   5   6   7   8   9   10

Warning signs (hours to days prior)?

○ Mood change
○ Decreased concentration
○ Visual disturbance
○ Physical symptoms
○ Fatigue
○ Sensitivity to light, sounds, or smells
○ Neck discomfort
○ Difficult speaking/reading
○ Nausea
○ Change in bowel habits
○ Food cravings/thirst
○ Yawning
○ Other:_____

Headache symptoms?

○ Pain on one side
○ Pain on both sides
○ Throbbing pain
○ Constant pain
○ Sensitive to light
○ Sensitive to sound
○ Worse with movement
○ Nausea/vomiting
○ Nasal congestion
○ Feeling cold or warm
○ Sensitive to smell/touch
○ Neck pain
○ Visual or other physical symptoms
○ Other:_____

Potential triggers?

○ Diet change
○ Change in water/caffeine/alcohol intake
○ Decreased sleep
○ Medication change
○ Increased stress
○ Weather
○ Amount of light
○ Strong smells
○ Loud sounds
○ Hormone change
○ Pressure on head
○ Vitamin/mineral deficiency
○ Change in exercise
○ Travel
○ Other:_____

Feelings afterward?

○ Feel normal
○ Depressed
○ Very happy
○ Fatigued
○ Decreased concentration
○ Other:_____

Additional details of headache:

Date:_____ Time:_____

How long did the headache last:_____

How severe is the pain? (Circle a number)

1   2   3   4   5   6   7   8   9   10

Warning signs (hours to days prior)?

Mood change
Decreased concentration
Visual disturbance
Physical symptoms
Fatigue
Sensitivity to light, sounds, or smells
Neck discomfort
Difficult speaking/reading
Nausea
Change in bowel habits
Food cravings/thirst
Yawning
Other:_____

Headache symptoms?

Pain on one side
Pain on both sides
Throbbing pain
Constant pain
Sensitive to light
Sensitive to sound
Worse with movement
Nausea/vomiting
Nasal congestion
Feeling cold or warm
Sensitive to smell/touch
Neck pain
Visual or other physical symptoms
Other:_____

Potential triggers?

Diet change
Change in water/caffeine/alcohol intake
Decreased sleep
Medication change
Increased stress
Weather
Amount of light
Strong smells
Loud sounds
Hormone change
Pressure on head
Vitamin/mineral deficiency
Change in exercise
Travel
Other:_____

Feelings afterward?

Feel normal
Depressed
Very happy
Fatigued
Decreased concentration
Other:_____

Additional details of headache:

Date:_____ Time:_____

How long did the headache last:_____

How severe is the pain? (Circle a number)

1 2 3 4 5 6 7 8 9 10

Warning signs (hours to days prior)?

- ◯ Mood change
- ◯ Decreased concentration
- ◯ Visual disturbance
- ◯ Physical symptoms
- ◯ Fatigue
- ◯ Sensitivity to light, sounds, or smells
- ◯ Neck discomfort
- ◯ Difficult speaking/reading
- ◯ Nausea
- ◯ Change in bowel habits
- ◯ Food cravings/thirst
- ◯ Yawning
- ◯ Other:_____

Headache symptoms?

- ◯ Pain on one side
- ◯ Pain on both sides
- ◯ Throbbing pain
- ◯ Constant pain
- ◯ Sensitive to light
- ◯ Sensitive to sound
- ◯ Worse with movement
- ◯ Nausea/vomiting
- ◯ Nasal congestion
- ◯ Feeling cold or warm
- ◯ Sensitive to smell/touch
- ◯ Neck pain
- ◯ Visual or other physical symptoms
- ◯ Other:_____

Potential triggers?

- ◯ Diet change
- ◯ Change in water/caffeine/alcohol intake
- ◯ Decreased sleep
- ◯ Medication change
- ◯ Increased stress
- ◯ Weather
- ◯ Amount of light
- ◯ Strong smells
- ◯ Loud sounds
- ◯ Hormone change
- ◯ Pressure on head
- ◯ Vitamin/mineral deficiency
- ◯ Change in exercise
- ◯ Travel
- ◯ Other:_____

Feelings afterward?

- ◯ Feel normal
- ◯ Depressed
- ◯ Very happy
- ◯ Fatigued
- ◯ Decreased concentration
- ◯ Other:_____

Additional details of headache:

Date:_____ Time:_____

How long did the headache last:_____

How severe is the pain? (Circle a number)

1 2 3 4 5 6 7 8 9 10

Warning signs (hours to days prior)?

- Mood change
- Decreased concentration
- Visual disturbance
- Physical symptoms
- Fatigue
- Sensitivity to light, sounds, or smells
- Neck discomfort
- Difficult speaking/reading
- Nausea
- Change in bowel habits
- Food cravings/thirst
- Yawning
- Other:_____

Headache symptoms?

- Pain on one side
- Pain on both sides
- Throbbing pain
- Constant pain
- Sensitive to light
- Sensitive to sound
- Worse with movement
- Nausea/vomiting
- Nasal congestion
- Feeling cold or warm
- Sensitive to smell/touch
- Neck pain
- Visual or other physical symptoms
- Other:_____

Potential triggers?

- Diet change
- Change in water/caffeine/alcohol intake
- Decreased sleep
- Medication change
- Increased stress
- Weather
- Amount of light
- Strong smells
- Loud sounds
- Hormone change
- Pressure on head
- Vitamin/mineral deficiency
- Change in exercise
- Travel
- Other:_____

Feelings afterward?

- Feel normal
- Depressed
- Very happy
- Fatigued
- Decreased concentration
- Other:_____

Additional details of headache:

Date:_____ Time:_____

How long did the headache last:_____

How severe is the pain? (Circle a number)

1 2 3 4 5 6 7 8 9 10

Warning signs (hours to days prior)?

- Mood change
- Decreased concentration
- Visual disturbance
- Physical symptoms
- Fatigue
- Sensitivity to light, sounds, or smells
- Neck discomfort
- Difficult speaking/reading
- Nausea
- Change in bowel habits
- Food cravings/thirst
- Yawning
- Other:_____

Headache symptoms?

- Pain on one side
- Pain on both sides
- Throbbing pain
- Constant pain
- Sensitive to light
- Sensitive to sound
- Worse with movement
- Nausea/vomiting
- Nasal congestion
- Feeling cold or warm
- Sensitive to smell/touch
- Neck pain
- Visual or other physical symptoms
- Other:_____

Potential triggers?

- Diet change
- Change in water/caffeine/alcohol intake
- Decreased sleep
- Medication change
- Increased stress
- Weather
- Amount of light
- Strong smells
- Loud sounds
- Hormone change
- Pressure on head
- Vitamin/mineral deficiency
- Change in exercise
- Travel
- Other:_____

Feelings afterward?

- Feel normal
- Depressed
- Very happy
- Fatigued
- Decreased concentration
- Other:_____

Additional details of headache:

Date:_____ Time:_____

How long did the headache last:_____

How severe is the pain? (Circle a number)

1   2   3   4   5   6   7   8   9   10

Warning signs (hours to days prior)?

- Mood change
- Decreased concentration
- Visual disturbance
- Physical symptoms
- Fatigue
- Sensitivity to light, sounds, or smells
- Neck discomfort
- Difficult speaking/reading
- Nausea
- Change in bowel habits
- Food cravings/thirst
- Yawning
- Other:_____

Headache symptoms?

- Pain on one side
- Pain on both sides
- Throbbing pain
- Constant pain
- Sensitive to light
- Sensitive to sound
- Worse with movement
- Nausea/vomiting
- Nasal congestion
- Feeling cold or warm
- Sensitive to smell/touch
- Neck pain
- Visual or other physical symptoms
- Other:_____

Potential triggers?

- Diet change
- Change in water/caffeine/alcohol intake
- Decreased sleep
- Medication change
- Increased stress
- Weather
- Amount of light
- Strong smells
- Loud sounds
- Hormone change
- Pressure on head
- Vitamin/mineral deficiency
- Change in exercise
- Travel
- Other:_____

Feelings afterward?

- Feel normal
- Depressed
- Very happy
- Fatigued
- Decreased concentration
- Other:_____

Additional details of headache:

Date:_____ Time:_____

How long did the headache last:_____

How severe is the pain? (Circle a number)

1 2 3 4 5 6 7 8 9 10

Warning signs (hours to days prior)?

- Mood change
- Decreased concentration
- Visual disturbance
- Physical symptoms
- Fatigue
- Sensitivity to light, sounds, or smells
- Neck discomfort
- Difficult speaking/reading
- Nausea
- Change in bowel habits
- Food cravings/thirst
- Yawning
- Other:_____

Headache symptoms?

- Pain on one side
- Pain on both sides
- Throbbing pain
- Constant pain
- Sensitive to light
- Sensitive to sound
- Worse with movement
- Nausea/vomiting
- Nasal congestion
- Feeling cold or warm
- Sensitive to smell/touch
- Neck pain
- Visual or other physical symptoms
- Other:_____

Potential triggers?

- Diet change
- Change in water/caffeine/alcohol intake
- Decreased sleep
- Medication change
- Increased stress
- Weather
- Amount of light
- Strong smells
- Loud sounds
- Hormone change
- Pressure on head
- Vitamin/mineral deficiency
- Change in exercise
- Travel
- Other:_____

Feelings afterward?

- Feel normal
- Depressed
- Very happy
- Fatigued
- Decreased concentration
- Other:_____

Additional details of headache:

Date:_____ Time:_____

How long did the headache last:_____

How severe is the pain? (Circle a number)

1　2　3　4　5　6　7　8　9　10

Warning signs (hours to days prior)?

- Mood change
- Decreased concentration
- Visual disturbance
- Physical symptoms
- Fatigue
- Sensitivity to light, sounds, or smells
- Neck discomfort
- Difficult speaking/reading
- Nausea
- Change in bowel habits
- Food cravings/thirst
- Yawning
- Other:_____

Headache symptoms?

- Pain on one side
- Pain on both sides
- Throbbing pain
- Constant pain
- Sensitive to light
- Sensitive to sound
- Worse with movement
- Nausea/vomiting
- Nasal congestion
- Feeling cold or warm
- Sensitive to smell/touch
- Neck pain
- Visual or other physical symptoms
- Other:_____

Potential triggers?

- Diet change
- Change in water/caffeine/alcohol intake
- Decreased sleep
- Medication change
- Increased stress
- Weather
- Amount of light
- Strong smells
- Loud sounds
- Hormone change
- Pressure on head
- Vitamin/mineral deficiency
- Change in exercise
- Travel
- Other:_____

Feelings afterward?

- Feel normal
- Depressed
- Very happy
- Fatigued
- Decreased concentration
- Other:_____

Additional details of headache:

Date:_____ Time:_____

How long did the headache last:_____

How severe is the pain? (Circle a number)

1 2 3 4 5 6 7 8 9 10

Warning signs (hours to days prior)?

- ○ Mood change
- ○ Decreased concentration
- ○ Visual disturbance
- ○ Physical symptoms
- ○ Fatigue
- ○ Sensitivity to light, sounds, or smells
- ○ Neck discomfort
- ○ Difficult speaking/reading
- ○ Nausea
- ○ Change in bowel habits
- ○ Food cravings/thirst
- ○ Yawning
- ○ Other:_____

Headache symptoms?

- ○ Pain on one side
- ○ Pain on both sides
- ○ Throbbing pain
- ○ Constant pain
- ○ Sensitive to light
- ○ Sensitive to sound
- ○ Worse with movement
- ○ Nausea/vomiting
- ○ Nasal congestion
- ○ Feeling cold or warm
- ○ Sensitive to smell/touch
- ○ Neck pain
- ○ Visual or other physical symptoms
- ○ Other:_____

Potential triggers?

- ○ Diet change
- ○ Change in water/caffeine/alcohol intake
- ○ Decreased sleep
- ○ Medication change
- ○ Increased stress
- ○ Weather
- ○ Amount of light
- ○ Strong smells
- ○ Loud sounds
- ○ Hormone change
- ○ Pressure on head
- ○ Vitamin/mineral deficiency
- ○ Change in exercise
- ○ Travel
- ○ Other:_____

Feelings afterward?

- ○ Feel normal
- ○ Depressed
- ○ Very happy
- ○ Fatigued
- ○ Decreased concentration
- ○ Other:_____

Additional details of headache:

Date:_____ Time:_____

How long did the headache last:_____

How severe is the pain? (Circle a number)

1 2 3 4 5 6 7 8 9 10

Warning signs (hours to days prior)?

○ Mood change
○ Decreased concentration
○ Visual disturbance
○ Physical symptoms
○ Fatigue
○ Sensitivity to light, sounds, or smells
○ Neck discomfort
○ Difficult speaking/reading
○ Nausea
○ Change in bowel habits
○ Food cravings/thirst
○ Yawning
○ Other:_____

Headache symptoms?

○ Pain on one side
○ Pain on both sides
○ Throbbing pain
○ Constant pain
○ Sensitive to light
○ Sensitive to sound
○ Worse with movement
○ Nausea/vomiting
○ Nasal congestion
○ Feeling cold or warm
○ Sensitive to smell/touch
○ Neck pain
○ Visual or other physical symptoms
○ Other:_____

Potential triggers?

○ Diet change
○ Change in water/caffeine/alcohol intake
○ Decreased sleep
○ Medication change
○ Increased stress
○ Weather
○ Amount of light
○ Strong smells
○ Loud sounds
○ Hormone change
○ Pressure on head
○ Vitamin/mineral deficiency
○ Change in exercise
○ Travel
○ Other:_____

Feelings afterward?

○ Feel normal
○ Depressed
○ Very happy
○ Fatigued
○ Decreased concentration
○ Other:_____

Additional details of headache:

Date:_____ Time:_____

How long did the headache last:_____

How severe is the pain? (Circle a number)

1   2   3   4   5   6   7   8   9   10

Warning signs (hours to days prior)?

○ Mood change
○ Decreased concentration
○ Visual disturbance
○ Physical symptoms
○ Fatigue
○ Sensitivity to light, sounds, or smells
○ Neck discomfort
○ Difficult speaking/reading
○ Nausea
○ Change in bowel habits
○ Food cravings/thirst
○ Yawning
○ Other:_____

Headache symptoms?

○ Pain on one side
○ Pain on both sides
○ Throbbing pain
○ Constant pain
○ Sensitive to light
○ Sensitive to sound
○ Worse with movement
○ Nausea/vomiting
○ Nasal congestion
○ Feeling cold or warm
○ Sensitive to smell/touch
○ Neck pain
○ Visual or other physical symptoms
○ Other:_____

Potential triggers?

○ Diet change
○ Change in water/caffeine/alcohol intake
○ Decreased sleep
○ Medication change
○ Increased stress
○ Weather
○ Amount of light
○ Strong smells
○ Loud sounds
○ Hormone change
○ Pressure on head
○ Vitamin/mineral deficiency
○ Change in exercise
○ Travel
○ Other:_____

Feelings afterward?

○ Feel normal
○ Depressed
○ Very happy
○ Fatigued
○ Decreased concentration
○ Other:_____

Additional details of headache:

Date:_____ Time:_____

How long did the headache last:_____

How severe is the pain? (Circle a number)

1   2   3   4   5   6   7   8   9   10

Warning signs (hours to days prior)?

- Mood change
- Decreased concentration
- Visual disturbance
- Physical symptoms
- Fatigue
- Sensitivity to light, sounds, or smells
- Neck discomfort
- Difficult speaking/reading
- Nausea
- Change in bowel habits
- Food cravings/thirst
- Yawning
- Other:_____

Headache symptoms?

- Pain on one side
- Pain on both sides
- Throbbing pain
- Constant pain
- Sensitive to light
- Sensitive to sound
- Worse with movement
- Nausea/vomiting
- Nasal congestion
- Feeling cold or warm
- Sensitive to smell/touch
- Neck pain
- Visual or other physical symptoms
- Other:_____

Potential triggers?

- Diet change
- Change in water/caffeine/alcohol intake
- Decreased sleep
- Medication change
- Increased stress
- Weather
- Amount of light
- Strong smells
- Loud sounds
- Hormone change
- Pressure on head
- Vitamin/mineral deficiency
- Change in exercise
- Travel
- Other:_____

Feelings afterward?

- Feel normal
- Depressed
- Very happy
- Fatigued
- Decreased concentration
- Other:_____

Additional details of headache:

Date:_____ Time:_____

How long did the headache last:_____

How severe is the pain? (Circle a number)

1   2   3   4   5   6   7   8   9   10

Warning signs (hours to days prior)?

○ Mood change
○ Decreased concentration
○ Visual disturbance
○ Physical symptoms
○ Fatigue
○ Sensitivity to light, sounds, or smells
○ Neck discomfort
○ Difficult speaking/reading
○ Nausea
○ Change in bowel habits
○ Food cravings/thirst
○ Yawning
○ Other:_____

Headache symptoms?

○ Pain on one side
○ Pain on both sides
○ Throbbing pain
○ Constant pain
○ Sensitive to light
○ Sensitive to sound
○ Worse with movement
○ Nausea/vomiting
○ Nasal congestion
○ Feeling cold or warm
○ Sensitive to smell/touch
○ Neck pain
○ Visual or other physical symptoms
○ Other:_____

Potential triggers?

○ Diet change
○ Change in water/caffeine/alcohol intake
○ Decreased sleep
○ Medication change
○ Increased stress
○ Weather
○ Amount of light
○ Strong smells
○ Loud sounds
○ Hormone change
○ Pressure on head
○ Vitamin/mineral deficiency
○ Change in exercise
○ Travel
○ Other:_____

Feelings afterward?

○ Feel normal
○ Depressed
○ Very happy
○ Fatigued
○ Decreased concentration
○ Other:_____

Additional details of headache:

Date:_____ Time:_____

How long did the headache last:_____

How severe is the pain? (Circle a number)

1 2 3 4 5 6 7 8 9 10

Warning signs (hours to days prior)?

- Mood change
- Decreased concentration
- Visual disturbance
- Physical symptoms
- Fatigue
- Sensitivity to light, sounds, or smells
- Neck discomfort
- Difficult speaking/reading
- Nausea
- Change in bowel habits
- Food cravings/thirst
- Yawning
- Other:_____

Headache symptoms?

- Pain on one side
- Pain on both sides
- Throbbing pain
- Constant pain
- Sensitive to light
- Sensitive to sound
- Worse with movement
- Nausea/vomiting
- Nasal congestion
- Feeling cold or warm
- Sensitive to smell/touch
- Neck pain
- Visual or other physical symptoms
- Other:_____

Potential triggers?

- Diet change
- Change in water/caffeine/alcohol intake
- Decreased sleep
- Medication change
- Increased stress
- Weather
- Amount of light
- Strong smells
- Loud sounds
- Hormone change
- Pressure on head
- Vitamin/mineral deficiency
- Change in exercise
- Travel
- Other:_____

Feelings afterward?

- Feel normal
- Depressed
- Very happy
- Fatigued
- Decreased concentration
- Other:_____

Additional details of headache:

Date:_____ Time:_____

How long did the headache last:_____

How severe is the pain? (Circle a number)

1   2   3   4   5   6   7   8   9   10

Warning signs (hours to days prior)?

- Mood change
- Decreased concentration
- Visual disturbance
- Physical symptoms
- Fatigue
- Sensitivity to light, sounds, or smells
- Neck discomfort
- Difficult speaking/reading
- Nausea
- Change in bowel habits
- Food cravings/thirst
- Yawning
- Other:_____

Headache symptoms?

- Pain on one side
- Pain on both sides
- Throbbing pain
- Constant pain
- Sensitive to light
- Sensitive to sound
- Worse with movement
- Nausea/vomiting
- Nasal congestion
- Feeling cold or warm
- Sensitive to smell/touch
- Neck pain
- Visual or other physical symptoms
- Other:_____

Potential triggers?

- Diet change
- Change in water/caffeine/alcohol intake
- Decreased sleep
- Medication change
- Increased stress
- Weather
- Amount of light
- Strong smells
- Loud sounds
- Hormone change
- Pressure on head
- Vitamin/mineral deficiency
- Change in exercise
- Travel
- Other:_____

Feelings afterward?

- Feel normal
- Depressed
- Very happy
- Fatigued
- Decreased concentration
- Other:_____

Additional details of headache:

Date:_____ Time:_____

How long did the headache last:_____

How severe is the pain? (Circle a number)

1   2   3   4   5   6   7   8   9   10

Warning signs (hours to days prior)?

Mood change
Decreased concentration
Visual disturbance
Physical symptoms
Fatigue
Sensitivity to light, sounds, or smells
Neck discomfort
Difficult speaking/reading
Nausea
Change in bowel habits
Food cravings/thirst
Yawning
Other:_____

Headache symptoms?

Pain on one side
Pain on both sides
Throbbing pain
Constant pain
Sensitive to light
Sensitive to sound
Worse with movement
Nausea/vomiting
Nasal congestion
Feeling cold or warm
Sensitive to smell/touch
Neck pain
Visual or other physical symptoms
Other:_____

Potential triggers?

Diet change
Change in water/caffeine/alcohol intake
Decreased sleep
Medication change
Increased stress
Weather
Amount of light
Strong smells
Loud sounds
Hormone change
Pressure on head
Vitamin/mineral deficiency
Change in exercise
Travel
Other:_____

Feelings afterward?

Feel normal
Depressed
Very happy
Fatigued
Decreased concentration
Other:_____

Additional details of headache:

Date:_____ Time:_____

How long did the headache last:_____

How severe is the pain? (Circle a number)

1 2 3 4 5 6 7 8 9 10

Warning signs (hours to days prior)?

- ⚪ Mood change
- ⚪ Decreased concentration
- ⚪ Visual disturbance
- ⚪ Physical symptoms
- ⚪ Fatigue
- ⚪ Sensitivity to light, sounds, or smells
- ⚪ Neck discomfort
- ⚪ Difficult speaking/reading
- ⚪ Nausea
- ⚪ Change in bowel habits
- ⚪ Food cravings/thirst
- ⚪ Yawning
- ⚪ Other:_____

Headache symptoms?

- ⚪ Pain on one side
- ⚪ Pain on both sides
- ⚪ Throbbing pain
- ⚪ Constant pain
- ⚪ Sensitive to light
- ⚪ Sensitive to sound
- ⚪ Worse with movement
- ⚪ Nausea/vomiting
- ⚪ Nasal congestion
- ⚪ Feeling cold or warm
- ⚪ Sensitive to smell/touch
- ⚪ Neck pain
- ⚪ Visual or other physical symptoms
- ⚪ Other:_____

Potential triggers?

- ⚪ Diet change
- ⚪ Change in water/caffeine/alcohol intake
- ⚪ Decreased sleep
- ⚪ Medication change
- ⚪ Increased stress
- ⚪ Weather
- ⚪ Amount of light
- ⚪ Strong smells
- ⚪ Loud sounds
- ⚪ Hormone change
- ⚪ Pressure on head
- ⚪ Vitamin/mineral deficiency
- ⚪ Change in exercise
- ⚪ Travel
- ⚪ Other:_____

Feelings afterward?

- ⚪ Feel normal
- ⚪ Depressed
- ⚪ Very happy
- ⚪ Fatigued
- ⚪ Decreased concentration
- ⚪ Other:_____

Additional details of headache:

Date:_____ Time:_____

How long did the headache last:_____

How severe is the pain? (Circle a number)

1 2 3 4 5 6 7 8 9 10

Warning signs
(hours to days prior)?

- Mood change
- Decreased concentration
- Visual disturbance
- Physical symptoms
- Fatigue
- Sensitivity to light, sounds, or smells
- Neck discomfort
- Difficult speaking/reading
- Nausea
- Change in bowel habits
- Food cravings/thirst
- Yawning
- Other:_____

Headache symptoms?

- Pain on one side
- Pain on both sides
- Throbbing pain
- Constant pain
- Sensitive to light
- Sensitive to sound
- Worse with movement
- Nausea/vomiting
- Nasal congestion
- Feeling cold or warm
- Sensitive to smell/touch
- Neck pain
- Visual or other physical symptoms
- Other:_____

Potential triggers?

- Diet change
- Change in water/caffeine/alcohol intake
- Decreased sleep
- Medication change
- Increased stress
- Weather
- Amount of light
- Strong smells
- Loud sounds
- Hormone change
- Pressure on head
- Vitamin/mineral deficiency
- Change in exercise
- Travel
- Other:_____

Feelings afterward?

- Feel normal
- Depressed
- Very happy
- Fatigued
- Decreased concentration
- Other:_____

Additional details of headache:

Date:_____ Time:_____

How long did the headache last:_____

How severe is the pain? (Circle a number)

1 2 3 4 5 6 7 8 9 10

Warning signs (hours to days prior)?

- ○ Mood change
- ○ Decreased concentration
- ○ Visual disturbance
- ○ Physical symptoms
- ○ Fatigue
- ○ Sensitivity to light, sounds, or smells
- ○ Neck discomfort
- ○ Difficult speaking/reading
- ○ Nausea
- ○ Change in bowel habits
- ○ Food cravings/thirst
- ○ Yawning
- ○ Other:_____

Headache symptoms?

- ○ Pain on one side
- ○ Pain on both sides
- ○ Throbbing pain
- ○ Constant pain
- ○ Sensitive to light
- ○ Sensitive to sound
- ○ Worse with movement
- ○ Nausea/vomiting
- ○ Nasal congestion
- ○ Feeling cold or warm
- ○ Sensitive to smell/touch
- ○ Neck pain
- ○ Visual or other physical symptoms
- ○ Other:_____

Potential triggers?

- ○ Diet change
- ○ Change in water/caffeine/alcohol intake
- ○ Decreased sleep
- ○ Medication change
- ○ Increased stress
- ○ Weather
- ○ Amount of light
- ○ Strong smells
- ○ Loud sounds
- ○ Hormone change
- ○ Pressure on head
- ○ Vitamin/mineral deficiency
- ○ Change in exercise
- ○ Travel
- ○ Other:_____

Feelings afterward?

- ○ Feel normal
- ○ Depressed
- ○ Very happy
- ○ Fatigued
- ○ Decreased concentration
- ○ Other:_____

Additional details of headache:

Date:_____ Time:_____

How long did the headache last:_____

How severe is the pain? (Circle a number)

1 2 3 4 5 6 7 8 9 10

Warning signs (hours to days prior)?

Mood change
Decreased concentration
Visual disturbance
Physical symptoms
Fatigue
Sensitivity to light, sounds, or smells
Neck discomfort
Difficult speaking/reading
Nausea
Change in bowel habits
Food cravings/thirst
Yawning
Other:_____

Potential triggers?

Diet change
Change in water/caffeine/alcohol intake
Decreased sleep
Medication change
Increased stress
Weather
Amount of light
Strong smells
Loud sounds
Hormone change
Pressure on head
Vitamin/mineral deficiency
Change in exercise
Travel
Other:_____

Headache symptoms?

Pain on one side
Pain on both sides
Throbbing pain
Constant pain
Sensitive to light
Sensitive to sound
Worse with movement
Nausea/vomiting
Nasal congestion
Feeling cold or warm
Sensitive to smell/touch
Neck pain
Visual or other physical symptoms
Other:_____

Feelings afterward?

Feel normal
Depressed
Very happy
Fatigued
Decreased concentration
Other:_____

Additional details of headache:

Date:_____ Time:_____

How long did the headache last:_____

How severe is the pain? (Circle a number)

1   2   3   4   5   6   7   8   9   10

Warning signs (hours to days prior)?

○ Mood change
○ Decreased concentration
○ Visual disturbance
○ Physical symptoms
○ Fatigue
○ Sensitivity to light, sounds, or smells
○ Neck discomfort
○ Difficult speaking/reading
○ Nausea
○ Change in bowel habits
○ Food cravings/thirst
○ Yawning
○ Other:_____

Headache symptoms?

○ Pain on one side
○ Pain on both sides
○ Throbbing pain
○ Constant pain
○ Sensitive to light
○ Sensitive to sound
○ Worse with movement
○ Nausea/vomiting
○ Nasal congestion
○ Feeling cold or warm
○ Sensitive to smell/touch
○ Neck pain
○ Visual or other physical symptoms
○ Other:_____

Potential triggers?

○ Diet change
○ Change in water/caffeine/alcohol intake
○ Decreased sleep
○ Medication change
○ Increased stress
○ Weather
○ Amount of light
○ Strong smells
○ Loud sounds
○ Hormone change
○ Pressure on head
○ Vitamin/mineral deficiency
○ Change in exercise
○ Travel
○ Other:_____

Feelings afterward?

○ Feel normal
○ Depressed
○ Very happy
○ Fatigued
○ Decreased concentration
○ Other:_____

Additional details of headache:

Date:_____ Time:_____

How long did the headache last:_____

How severe is the pain? (Circle a number)

1   2   3   4   5   6   7   8   9   10

Warning signs (hours to days prior)?

- Mood change
- Decreased concentration
- Visual disturbance
- Physical symptoms
- Fatigue
- Sensitivity to light, sounds, or smells
- Neck discomfort
- Difficult speaking/reading
- Nausea
- Change in bowel habits
- Food cravings/thirst
- Yawning
- Other:_____

Headache symptoms?

- Pain on one side
- Pain on both sides
- Throbbing pain
- Constant pain
- Sensitive to light
- Sensitive to sound
- Worse with movement
- Nausea/vomiting
- Nasal congestion
- Feeling cold or warm
- Sensitive to smell/touch
- Neck pain
- Visual or other physical symptoms
- Other:_____

Potential triggers?

- Diet change
- Change in water/caffeine/alcohol intake
- Decreased sleep
- Medication change
- Increased stress
- Weather
- Amount of light
- Strong smells
- Loud sounds
- Hormone change
- Pressure on head
- Vitamin/mineral deficiency
- Change in exercise
- Travel
- Other:_____

Feelings afterward?

- Feel normal
- Depressed
- Very happy
- Fatigued
- Decreased concentration
- Other:_____

Additional details of headache:

Date:_____ Time:_____

How long did the headache last:_____

How severe is the pain? (Circle a number)

1   2   3   4   5   6   7   8   9   10

Warning signs (hours to days prior)?

- Mood change
- Decreased concentration
- Visual disturbance
- Physical symptoms
- Fatigue
- Sensitivity to light, sounds, or smells
- Neck discomfort
- Difficult speaking/reading
- Nausea
- Change in bowel habits
- Food cravings/thirst
- Yawning
- Other:_____

Headache symptoms?

- Pain on one side
- Pain on both sides
- Throbbing pain
- Constant pain
- Sensitive to light
- Sensitive to sound
- Worse with movement
- Nausea/vomiting
- Nasal congestion
- Feeling cold or warm
- Sensitive to smell/touch
- Neck pain
- Visual or other physical symptoms
- Other:_____

Potential triggers?

- Diet change
- Change in water/caffeine/alcohol intake
- Decreased sleep
- Medication change
- Increased stress
- Weather
- Amount of light
- Strong smells
- Loud sounds
- Hormone change
- Pressure on head
- Vitamin/mineral deficiency
- Change in exercise
- Travel
- Other:_____

Feelings afterward?

- Feel normal
- Depressed
- Very happy
- Fatigued
- Decreased concentration
- Other:_____

Additional details of headache:

Date:_____ Time:_____

How long did the headache last:_____

How severe is the pain? (Circle a number)

1   2   3   4   5   6   7   8   9   10

Warning signs (hours to days prior)?

- Mood change
- Decreased concentration
- Visual disturbance
- Physical symptoms
- Fatigue
- Sensitivity to light, sounds, or smells
- Neck discomfort
- Difficult speaking/reading
- Nausea
- Change in bowel habits
- Food cravings/thirst
- Yawning
- Other:_____

Headache symptoms?

- Pain on one side
- Pain on both sides
- Throbbing pain
- Constant pain
- Sensitive to light
- Sensitive to sound
- Worse with movement
- Nausea/vomiting
- Nasal congestion
- Feeling cold or warm
- Sensitive to smell/touch
- Neck pain
- Visual or other physical symptoms
- Other:_____

Potential triggers?

- Diet change
- Change in water/caffeine/alcohol intake
- Decreased sleep
- Medication change
- Increased stress
- Weather
- Amount of light
- Strong smells
- Loud sounds
- Hormone change
- Pressure on head
- Vitamin/mineral deficiency
- Change in exercise
- Travel
- Other:_____

Feelings afterward?

- Feel normal
- Depressed
- Very happy
- Fatigued
- Decreased concentration
- Other:_____

Additional details of headache:

Date:_____ Time:_____

How long did the headache last:_____

How severe is the pain? (Circle a number)

1   2   3   4   5   6   7   8   9   10

Warning signs (hours to days prior)?

○ Mood change
○ Decreased concentration
○ Visual disturbance
○ Physical symptoms
○ Fatigue
○ Sensitivity to light, sounds, or smells
○ Neck discomfort
○ Difficult speaking/reading
○ Nausea
○ Change in bowel habits
○ Food cravings/thirst
○ Yawning
○ Other:_____

Headache symptoms?

○ Pain on one side
○ Pain on both sides
○ Throbbing pain
○ Constant pain
○ Sensitive to light
○ Sensitive to sound
○ Worse with movement
○ Nausea/vomiting
○ Nasal congestion
○ Feeling cold or warm
○ Sensitive to smell/touch
○ Neck pain
○ Visual or other physical symptoms
○ Other:_____

Potential triggers?

○ Diet change
○ Change in water/caffeine/alcohol intake
○ Decreased sleep
○ Medication change
○ Increased stress
○ Weather
○ Amount of light
○ Strong smells
○ Loud sounds
○ Hormone change
○ Pressure on head
○ Vitamin/mineral deficiency
○ Change in exercise
○ Travel
○ Other:_____

Feelings afterward?

○ Feel normal
○ Depressed
○ Very happy
○ Fatigued
○ Decreased concentration
○ Other:_____

Additional details of headache:

Date:_____ Time:_____

How long did the headache last:_____

How severe is the pain? (Circle a number)

1   2   3   4   5   6   7   8   9   10

Warning signs (hours to days prior)?

Mood change
Decreased concentration
Visual disturbance
Physical symptoms
Fatigue
Sensitivity to light, sounds, or smells
Neck discomfort
Difficult speaking/reading
Nausea
Change in bowel habits
Food cravings/thirst
Yawning
Other:_____

Potential triggers?

Diet change
Change in water/caffeine/alcohol intake
Decreased sleep
Medication change
Increased stress
Weather
Amount of light
Strong smells
Loud sounds
Hormone change
Pressure on head
Vitamin/mineral deficiency
Change in exercise
Travel
Other:_____

Headache symptoms?

Pain on one side
Pain on both sides
Throbbing pain
Constant pain
Sensitive to light
Sensitive to sound
Worse with movement
Nausea/vomiting
Nasal congestion
Feeling cold or warm
Sensitive to smell/touch
Neck pain
Visual or other physical symptoms
Other:_____

Feelings afterward?

Feel normal
Depressed
Very happy
Fatigued
Decreased concentration
Other:_____

Additional details of headache:

Date:_____ Time:_____

How long did the headache last:_____

How severe is the pain? (Circle a number)

1 2 3 4 5 6 7 8 9 10

Warning signs
(hours to days prior)?

- Mood change
- Decreased concentration
- Visual disturbance
- Physical symptoms
- Fatigue
- Sensitivity to light, sounds, or smells
- Neck discomfort
- Difficult speaking/reading
- Nausea
- Change in bowel habits
- Food cravings/thirst
- Yawning
- Other:_____

Headache symptoms?

- Pain on one side
- Pain on both sides
- Throbbing pain
- Constant pain
- Sensitive to light
- Sensitive to sound
- Worse with movement
- Nausea/vomiting
- Nasal congestion
- Feeling cold or warm
- Sensitive to smell/touch
- Neck pain
- Visual or other physical symptoms
- Other:_____

Potential triggers?

- Diet change
- Change in water/caffeine/alcohol intake
- Decreased sleep
- Medication change
- Increased stress
- Weather
- Amount of light
- Strong smells
- Loud sounds
- Hormone change
- Pressure on head
- Vitamin/mineral deficiency
- Change in exercise
- Travel
- Other:_____

Feelings afterward?

- Feel normal
- Depressed
- Very happy
- Fatigued
- Decreased concentration
- Other:_____

Additional details of headache:

Date:_____ Time:_____

How long did the headache last:_____

How severe is the pain? (Circle a number)

1   2   3   4   5   6   7   8   9   10

Warning signs (hours to days prior)?

Mood change
Decreased concentration
Visual disturbance
Physical symptoms
Fatigue
Sensitivity to light, sounds, or smells
Neck discomfort
Difficult speaking/reading
Nausea
Change in bowel habits
Food cravings/thirst
Yawning
Other:_____

Headache symptoms?

Pain on one side
Pain on both sides
Throbbing pain
Constant pain
Sensitive to light
Sensitive to sound
Worse with movement
Nausea/vomiting
Nasal congestion
Feeling cold or warm
Sensitive to smell/touch
Neck pain
Visual or other physical symptoms
Other:_____

Potential triggers?

Diet change
Change in water/caffeine/alcohol intake
Decreased sleep
Medication change
Increased stress
Weather
Amount of light
Strong smells
Loud sounds
Hormone change
Pressure on head
Vitamin/mineral deficiency
Change in exercise
Travel
Other:_____

Feelings afterward?

Feel normal
Depressed
Very happy
Fatigued
Decreased concentration
Other:_____

Additional details of headache:

Date:_____ Time:_____

How long did the headache last:_____

How severe is the pain? (Circle a number)

1 2 3 4 5 6 7 8 9 10

Warning signs (hours to days prior)?

- ○ Mood change
- ○ Decreased concentration
- ○ Visual disturbance
- ○ Physical symptoms
- ○ Fatigue
- ○ Sensitivity to light, sounds, or smells
- ○ Neck discomfort
- ○ Difficult speaking/reading
- ○ Nausea
- ○ Change in bowel habits
- ○ Food cravings/thirst
- ○ Yawning
- ○ Other:_____

Headache symptoms?

- ○ Pain on one side
- ○ Pain on both sides
- ○ Throbbing pain
- ○ Constant pain
- ○ Sensitive to light
- ○ Sensitive to sound
- ○ Worse with movement
- ○ Nausea/vomiting
- ○ Nasal congestion
- ○ Feeling cold or warm
- ○ Sensitive to smell/touch
- ○ Neck pain
- ○ Visual or other physical symptoms
- ○ Other:_____

Potential triggers?

- ○ Diet change
- ○ Change in water/caffeine/alcohol intake
- ○ Decreased sleep
- ○ Medication change
- ○ Increased stress
- ○ Weather
- ○ Amount of light
- ○ Strong smells
- ○ Loud sounds
- ○ Hormone change
- ○ Pressure on head
- ○ Vitamin/mineral deficiency
- ○ Change in exercise
- ○ Travel
- ○ Other:_____

Feelings afterward?

- ○ Feel normal
- ○ Depressed
- ○ Very happy
- ○ Fatigued
- ○ Decreased concentration
- ○ Other:_____

Additional details of headache:

Date:_____ Time:_____

How long did the headache last:_____

How severe is the pain? (Circle a number)

1 2 3 4 5 6 7 8 9 10

Warning signs (hours to days prior)?

- Mood change
- Decreased concentration
- Visual disturbance
- Physical symptoms
- Fatigue
- Sensitivity to light, sounds, or smells
- Neck discomfort
- Difficult speaking/reading
- Nausea
- Change in bowel habits
- Food cravings/thirst
- Yawning
- Other:_____

Headache symptoms?

- Pain on one side
- Pain on both sides
- Throbbing pain
- Constant pain
- Sensitive to light
- Sensitive to sound
- Worse with movement
- Nausea/vomiting
- Nasal congestion
- Feeling cold or warm
- Sensitive to smell/touch
- Neck pain
- Visual or other physical symptoms
- Other:_____

Potential triggers?

- Diet change
- Change in water/caffeine/alcohol intake
- Decreased sleep
- Medication change
- Increased stress
- Weather
- Amount of light
- Strong smells
- Loud sounds
- Hormone change
- Pressure on head
- Vitamin/mineral deficiency
- Change in exercise
- Travel
- Other:_____

Feelings afterward?

- Feel normal
- Depressed
- Very happy
- Fatigued
- Decreased concentration
- Other:_____

Additional details of headache:

Date:_____ Time:_____

How long did the headache last:_____

How severe is the pain? (Circle a number)

1   2   3   4   5   6   7   8   9   10

Warning signs (hours to days prior)?

- Mood change
- Decreased concentration
- Visual disturbance
- Physical symptoms
- Fatigue
- Sensitivity to light, sounds, or smells
- Neck discomfort
- Difficult speaking/reading
- Nausea
- Change in bowel habits
- Food cravings/thirst
- Yawning
- Other:_____

Headache symptoms?

- Pain on one side
- Pain on both sides
- Throbbing pain
- Constant pain
- Sensitive to light
- Sensitive to sound
- Worse with movement
- Nausea/vomiting
- Nasal congestion
- Feeling cold or warm
- Sensitive to smell/touch
- Neck pain
- Visual or other physical symptoms
- Other:_____

Potential triggers?

- Diet change
- Change in water/caffeine/alcohol intake
- Decreased sleep
- Medication change
- Increased stress
- Weather
- Amount of light
- Strong smells
- Loud sounds
- Hormone change
- Pressure on head
- Vitamin/mineral deficiency
- Change in exercise
- Travel
- Other:_____

Feelings afterward?

- Feel normal
- Depressed
- Very happy
- Fatigued
- Decreased concentration
- Other:_____

Additional details of headache:

Date:_____ Time:_____

How long did the headache last:_____

How severe is the pain? (Circle a number)

1 2 3 4 5 6 7 8 9 10

Warning signs (hours to days prior)?

- Mood change
- Decreased concentration
- Visual disturbance
- Physical symptoms
- Fatigue
- Sensitivity to light, sounds, or smells
- Neck discomfort
- Difficult speaking/reading
- Nausea
- Change in bowel habits
- Food cravings/thirst
- Yawning
- Other:_____

Headache symptoms?

- Pain on one side
- Pain on both sides
- Throbbing pain
- Constant pain
- Sensitive to light
- Sensitive to sound
- Worse with movement
- Nausea/vomiting
- Nasal congestion
- Feeling cold or warm
- Sensitive to smell/touch
- Neck pain
- Visual or other physical symptoms
- Other:_____

Potential triggers?

- Diet change
- Change in water/caffeine/alcohol intake
- Decreased sleep
- Medication change
- Increased stress
- Weather
- Amount of light
- Strong smells
- Loud sounds
- Hormone change
- Pressure on head
- Vitamin/mineral deficiency
- Change in exercise
- Travel
- Other:_____

Feelings afterward?

- Feel normal
- Depressed
- Very happy
- Fatigued
- Decreased concentration
- Other:_____

Additional details of headache:

Date:_____ Time:_____

How long did the headache last:_____

How severe is the pain? (Circle a number)

1 2 3 4 5 6 7 8 9 10

Warning signs (hours to days prior)?

- Mood change
- Decreased concentration
- Visual disturbance
- Physical symptoms
- Fatigue
- Sensitivity to light, sounds, or smells
- Neck discomfort
- Difficult speaking/reading
- Nausea
- Change in bowel habits
- Food cravings/thirst
- Yawning
- Other:_____

Headache symptoms?

- Pain on one side
- Pain on both sides
- Throbbing pain
- Constant pain
- Sensitive to light
- Sensitive to sound
- Worse with movement
- Nausea/vomiting
- Nasal congestion
- Feeling cold or warm
- Sensitive to smell/touch
- Neck pain
- Visual or other physical symptoms
- Other:_____

Potential triggers?

- Diet change
- Change in water/caffeine/alcohol intake
- Decreased sleep
- Medication change
- Increased stress
- Weather
- Amount of light
- Strong smells
- Loud sounds
- Hormone change
- Pressure on head
- Vitamin/mineral deficiency
- Change in exercise
- Travel
- Other:_____

Feelings afterward?

- Feel normal
- Depressed
- Very happy
- Fatigued
- Decreased concentration
- Other:_____

Additional details of headache:

Date:_____ Time:_____

How long did the headache last:_____

How severe is the pain? (Circle a number)

1 2 3 4 5 6 7 8 9 10

Warning signs (hours to days prior)?

- Mood change
- Decreased concentration
- Visual disturbance
- Physical symptoms
- Fatigue
- Sensitivity to light, sounds, or smells
- Neck discomfort
- Difficult speaking/reading
- Nausea
- Change in bowel habits
- Food cravings/thirst
- Yawning
- Other:_____

Headache symptoms?

- Pain on one side
- Pain on both sides
- Throbbing pain
- Constant pain
- Sensitive to light
- Sensitive to sound
- Worse with movement
- Nausea/vomiting
- Nasal congestion
- Feeling cold or warm
- Sensitive to smell/touch
- Neck pain
- Visual or other physical symptoms
- Other:_____

Potential triggers?

- Diet change
- Change in water/caffeine/alcohol intake
- Decreased sleep
- Medication change
- Increased stress
- Weather
- Amount of light
- Strong smells
- Loud sounds
- Hormone change
- Pressure on head
- Vitamin/mineral deficiency
- Change in exercise
- Travel
- Other:_____

Feelings afterward?

- Feel normal
- Depressed
- Very happy
- Fatigued
- Decreased concentration
- Other:_____

Additional details of headache:

Date:_____ Time:_____

How long did the headache last:_____

How severe is the pain? (Circle a number)

1 2 3 4 5 6 7 8 9 10

Warning signs (hours to days prior)?

- ○ Mood change
- ○ Decreased concentration
- ○ Visual disturbance
- ○ Physical symptoms
- ○ Fatigue
- ○ Sensitivity to light, sounds, or smells
- ○ Neck discomfort
- ○ Difficult speaking/reading
- ○ Nausea
- ○ Change in bowel habits
- ○ Food cravings/thirst
- ○ Yawning
- ○ Other:_____

Headache symptoms?

- ○ Pain on one side
- ○ Pain on both sides
- ○ Throbbing pain
- ○ Constant pain
- ○ Sensitive to light
- ○ Sensitive to sound
- ○ Worse with movement
- ○ Nausea/vomiting
- ○ Nasal congestion
- ○ Feeling cold or warm
- ○ Sensitive to smell/touch
- ○ Neck pain
- ○ Visual or other physical symptoms
- ○ Other:_____

Potential triggers?

- ○ Diet change
- ○ Change in water/caffeine/alcohol intake
- ○ Decreased sleep
- ○ Medication change
- ○ Increased stress
- ○ Weather
- ○ Amount of light
- ○ Strong smells
- ○ Loud sounds
- ○ Hormone change
- ○ Pressure on head
- ○ Vitamin/mineral deficiency
- ○ Change in exercise
- ○ Travel
- ○ Other:_____

Feelings afterward?

- ○ Feel normal
- ○ Depressed
- ○ Very happy
- ○ Fatigued
- ○ Decreased concentration
- ○ Other:_____

Additional details of headache:

Date:_____ Time:_____

How long did the headache last:_____

How severe is the pain? (Circle a number)

1   2   3   4   5   6   7   8   9   10

Warning signs (hours to days prior)?

Mood change
Decreased concentration
Visual disturbance
Physical symptoms
Fatigue
Sensitivity to light, sounds, or smells
Neck discomfort
Difficult speaking/reading
Nausea
Change in bowel habits
Food cravings/thirst
Yawning
Other:_____

Headache symptoms?

Pain on one side
Pain on both sides
Throbbing pain
Constant pain
Sensitive to light
Sensitive to sound
Worse with movement
Nausea/vomiting
Nasal congestion
Feeling cold or warm
Sensitive to smell/touch
Neck pain
Visual or other physical symptoms
Other:_____

Potential triggers?

Diet change
Change in water/caffeine/alcohol intake
Decreased sleep
Medication change
Increased stress
Weather
Amount of light
Strong smells
Loud sounds
Hormone change
Pressure on head
Vitamin/mineral deficiency
Change in exercise
Travel
Other:_____

Feelings afterward?

Feel normal
Depressed
Very happy
Fatigued
Decreased concentration
Other:_____

Additional details of headache:

Date:_____ Time:_____

How long did the headache last:_____

How severe is the pain? (Circle a number)

1 2 3 4 5 6 7 8 9 10

Warning signs (hours to days prior)?

- ○ Mood change
- ○ Decreased concentration
- ○ Visual disturbance
- ○ Physical symptoms
- ○ Fatigue
- ○ Sensitivity to light, sounds, or smells
- ○ Neck discomfort
- ○ Difficult speaking/reading
- ○ Nausea
- ○ Change in bowel habits
- ○ Food cravings/thirst
- ○ Yawning
- ○ Other:_____

Headache symptoms?

- ○ Pain on one side
- ○ Pain on both sides
- ○ Throbbing pain
- ○ Constant pain
- ○ Sensitive to light
- ○ Sensitive to sound
- ○ Worse with movement
- ○ Nausea/vomiting
- ○ Nasal congestion
- ○ Feeling cold or warm
- ○ Sensitive to smell/touch
- ○ Neck pain
- ○ Visual or other physical symptoms
- ○ Other:_____

Potential triggers?

- ○ Diet change
- ○ Change in water/caffeine/alcohol intake
- ○ Decreased sleep
- ○ Medication change
- ○ Increased stress
- ○ Weather
- ○ Amount of light
- ○ Strong smells
- ○ Loud sounds
- ○ Hormone change
- ○ Pressure on head
- ○ Vitamin/mineral deficiency
- ○ Change in exercise
- ○ Travel
- ○ Other:_____

Feelings afterward?

- ○ Feel normal
- ○ Depressed
- ○ Very happy
- ○ Fatigued
- ○ Decreased concentration
- ○ Other:_____

Additional details of headache:

Date:_____ Time:_____

How long did the headache last:_____

How severe is the pain? (Circle a number)

1 2 3 4 5 6 7 8 9 10

Warning signs (hours to days prior)?

Mood change
Decreased concentration
Visual disturbance
Physical symptoms
Fatigue
Sensitivity to light, sounds, or smells
Neck discomfort
Difficult speaking/reading
Nausea
Change in bowel habits
Food cravings/thirst
Yawning
Other:_____

Headache symptoms?

Pain on one side
Pain on both sides
Throbbing pain
Constant pain
Sensitive to light
Sensitive to sound
Worse with movement
Nausea/vomiting
Nasal congestion
Feeling cold or warm
Sensitive to smell/touch
Neck pain
Visual or other physical symptoms
Other:_____

Potential triggers?

Diet change
Change in water/caffeine/alcohol intake
Decreased sleep
Medication change
Increased stress
Weather
Amount of light
Strong smells
Loud sounds
Hormone change
Pressure on head
Vitamin/mineral deficiency
Change in exercise
Travel
Other:_____

Feelings afterward?

Feel normal
Depressed
Very happy
Fatigued
Decreased concentration
Other:_____

Additional details of headache:

Date:_____ Time:_____

How long did the headache last:_____

How severe is the pain? (Circle a number)

1 2 3 4 5 6 7 8 9 10

Warning signs (hours to days prior)?

- ◯ Mood change
- ◯ Decreased concentration
- ◯ Visual disturbance
- ◯ Physical symptoms
- ◯ Fatigue
- ◯ Sensitivity to light, sounds, or smells
- ◯ Neck discomfort
- ◯ Difficult speaking/reading
- ◯ Nausea
- ◯ Change in bowel habits
- ◯ Food cravings/thirst
- ◯ Yawning
- ◯ Other:_____

Headache symptoms?

- ◯ Pain on one side
- ◯ Pain on both sides
- ◯ Throbbing pain
- ◯ Constant pain
- ◯ Sensitive to light
- ◯ Sensitive to sound
- ◯ Worse with movement
- ◯ Nausea/vomiting
- ◯ Nasal congestion
- ◯ Feeling cold or warm
- ◯ Sensitive to smell/touch
- ◯ Neck pain
- ◯ Visual or other physical symptoms
- ◯ Other:_____

Potential triggers?

- ◯ Diet change
- ◯ Change in water/caffeine/alcohol intake
- ◯ Decreased sleep
- ◯ Medication change
- ◯ Increased stress
- ◯ Weather
- ◯ Amount of light
- ◯ Strong smells
- ◯ Loud sounds
- ◯ Hormone change
- ◯ Pressure on head
- ◯ Vitamin/mineral deficiency
- ◯ Change in exercise
- ◯ Travel
- ◯ Other:_____

Feelings afterward?

- ◯ Feel normal
- ◯ Depressed
- ◯ Very happy
- ◯ Fatigued
- ◯ Decreased concentration
- ◯ Other:_____

Additional details of headache:

Date:_____ Time:_____

How long did the headache last:_____

How severe is the pain? (Circle a number)

1 2 3 4 5 6 7 8 9 10

Warning signs (hours to days prior)?

- Mood change
- Decreased concentration
- Visual disturbance
- Physical symptoms
- Fatigue
- Sensitivity to light, sounds, or smells
- Neck discomfort
- Difficult speaking/reading
- Nausea
- Change in bowel habits
- Food cravings/thirst
- Yawning
- Other:_____

Headache symptoms?

- Pain on one side
- Pain on both sides
- Throbbing pain
- Constant pain
- Sensitive to light
- Sensitive to sound
- Worse with movement
- Nausea/vomiting
- Nasal congestion
- Feeling cold or warm
- Sensitive to smell/touch
- Neck pain
- Visual or other physical symptoms
- Other:_____

Potential triggers?

- Diet change
- Change in water/caffeine/alcohol intake
- Decreased sleep
- Medication change
- Increased stress
- Weather
- Amount of light
- Strong smells
- Loud sounds
- Hormone change
- Pressure on head
- Vitamin/mineral deficiency
- Change in exercise
- Travel
- Other:_____

Feelings afterward?

- Feel normal
- Depressed
- Very happy
- Fatigued
- Decreased concentration
- Other:_____

Additional details of headache:

Date:_____ Time:_____

How long did the headache last:_____

How severe is the pain? (Circle a number)

1   2   3   4   5   6   7   8   9   10

Warning signs (hours to days prior)?

○ Mood change
○ Decreased concentration
○ Visual disturbance
○ Physical symptoms
○ Fatigue
○ Sensitivity to light, sounds, or smells
○ Neck discomfort
○ Difficult speaking/reading
○ Nausea
○ Change in bowel habits
○ Food cravings/thirst
○ Yawning
○ Other:_____

Headache symptoms?

○ Pain on one side
○ Pain on both sides
○ Throbbing pain
○ Constant pain
○ Sensitive to light
○ Sensitive to sound
○ Worse with movement
○ Nausea/vomiting
○ Nasal congestion
○ Feeling cold or warm
○ Sensitive to smell/touch
○ Neck pain
○ Visual or other physical symptoms
○ Other:_____

Potential triggers?

○ Diet change
○ Change in water/caffeine/alcohol intake
○ Decreased sleep
○ Medication change
○ Increased stress
○ Weather
○ Amount of light
○ Strong smells
○ Loud sounds
○ Hormone change
○ Pressure on head
○ Vitamin/mineral deficiency
○ Change in exercise
○ Travel
○ Other:_____

Feelings afterward?

○ Feel normal
○ Depressed
○ Very happy
○ Fatigued
○ Decreased concentration
○ Other:_____

Additional details of headache:

Date:_____ Time:_____

How long did the headache last:_____

How severe is the pain? (Circle a number)

1   2   3   4   5   6   7   8   9   10

Warning signs (hours to days prior)?

- Mood change
- Decreased concentration
- Visual disturbance
- Physical symptoms
- Fatigue
- Sensitivity to light, sounds, or smells
- Neck discomfort
- Difficult speaking/reading
- Nausea
- Change in bowel habits
- Food cravings/thirst
- Yawning
- Other:_____

Headache symptoms?

- Pain on one side
- Pain on both sides
- Throbbing pain
- Constant pain
- Sensitive to light
- Sensitive to sound
- Worse with movement
- Nausea/vomiting
- Nasal congestion
- Feeling cold or warm
- Sensitive to smell/touch
- Neck pain
- Visual or other physical symptoms
- Other:_____

Potential triggers?

- Diet change
- Change in water/caffeine/alcohol intake
- Decreased sleep
- Medication change
- Increased stress
- Weather
- Amount of light
- Strong smells
- Loud sounds
- Hormone change
- Pressure on head
- Vitamin/mineral deficiency
- Change in exercise
- Travel
- Other:_____

Feelings afterward?

- Feel normal
- Depressed
- Very happy
- Fatigued
- Decreased concentration
- Other:_____

Additional details of headache:

Date:_____ Time:_____

How long did the headache last:_____

How severe is the pain? (Circle a number)

1   2   3   4   5   6   7   8   9   10

Warning signs (hours to days prior)?

- Mood change
- Decreased concentration
- Visual disturbance
- Physical symptoms
- Fatigue
- Sensitivity to light, sounds, or smells
- Neck discomfort
- Difficult speaking/reading
- Nausea
- Change in bowel habits
- Food cravings/thirst
- Yawning
- Other:_____

Headache symptoms?

- Pain on one side
- Pain on both sides
- Throbbing pain
- Constant pain
- Sensitive to light
- Sensitive to sound
- Worse with movement
- Nausea/vomiting
- Nasal congestion
- Feeling cold or warm
- Sensitive to smell/touch
- Neck pain
- Visual or other physical symptoms
- Other:_____

Potential triggers?

- Diet change
- Change in water/caffeine/alcohol intake
- Decreased sleep
- Medication change
- Increased stress
- Weather
- Amount of light
- Strong smells
- Loud sounds
- Hormone change
- Pressure on head
- Vitamin/mineral deficiency
- Change in exercise
- Travel
- Other:_____

Feelings afterward?

- Feel normal
- Depressed
- Very happy
- Fatigued
- Decreased concentration
- Other:_____

Additional details of headache:

Date:_____ Time:_____

How long did the headache last:_____

How severe is the pain? (Circle a number)

1   2   3   4   5   6   7   8   9   10

Warning signs (hours to days prior)?

Mood change
Decreased concentration
Visual disturbance
Physical symptoms
Fatigue
Sensitivity to light, sounds, or smells
Neck discomfort
Difficult speaking/reading
Nausea
Change in bowel habits
Food cravings/thirst
Yawning
Other:_____

Headache symptoms?

Pain on one side
Pain on both sides
Throbbing pain
Constant pain
Sensitive to light
Sensitive to sound
Worse with movement
Nausea/vomiting
Nasal congestion
Feeling cold or warm
Sensitive to smell/touch
Neck pain
Visual or other physical symptoms
Other:_____

Potential triggers?

Diet change
Change in water/caffeine/alcohol intake
Decreased sleep
Medication change
Increased stress
Weather
Amount of light
Strong smells
Loud sounds
Hormone change
Pressure on head
Vitamin/mineral deficiency
Change in exercise
Travel
Other:_____

Feelings afterward?

Feel normal
Depressed
Very happy
Fatigued
Decreased concentration
Other:_____

Additional details of headache:

Date:_____ Time:_____

How long did the headache last:_____

How severe is the pain? (Circle a number)

1 2 3 4 5 6 7 8 9 10

Warning signs (hours to days prior)?

- ○ Mood change
- ○ Decreased concentration
- ○ Visual disturbance
- ○ Physical symptoms
- ○ Fatigue
- ○ Sensitivity to light, sounds, or smells
- ○ Neck discomfort
- ○ Difficult speaking/reading
- ○ Nausea
- ○ Change in bowel habits
- ○ Food cravings/thirst
- ○ Yawning
- ○ Other:_____

Headache symptoms?

- ○ Pain on one side
- ○ Pain on both sides
- ○ Throbbing pain
- ○ Constant pain
- ○ Sensitive to light
- ○ Sensitive to sound
- ○ Worse with movement
- ○ Nausea/vomiting
- ○ Nasal congestion
- ○ Feeling cold or warm
- ○ Sensitive to smell/touch
- ○ Neck pain
- ○ Visual or other physical symptoms
- ○ Other:_____

Potential triggers?

- ○ Diet change
- ○ Change in water/caffeine/alcohol intake
- ○ Decreased sleep
- ○ Medication change
- ○ Increased stress
- ○ Weather
- ○ Amount of light
- ○ Strong smells
- ○ Loud sounds
- ○ Hormone change
- ○ Pressure on head
- ○ Vitamin/mineral deficiency
- ○ Change in exercise
- ○ Travel
- ○ Other:_____

Feelings afterward?

- ○ Feel normal
- ○ Depressed
- ○ Very happy
- ○ Fatigued
- ○ Decreased concentration
- ○ Other:_____

Additional details of headache:

Date:_____ Time:_____

How long did the headache last:_____

How severe is the pain? (Circle a number)

1   2   3   4   5   6   7   8   9   10

Warning signs (hours to days prior)?
- Mood change
- Decreased concentration
- Visual disturbance
- Physical symptoms
- Fatigue
- Sensitivity to light, sounds, or smells
- Neck discomfort
- Difficult speaking/reading
- Nausea
- Change in bowel habits
- Food cravings/thirst
- Yawning
- Other:_____

Headache symptoms?
- Pain on one side
- Pain on both sides
- Throbbing pain
- Constant pain
- Sensitive to light
- Sensitive to sound
- Worse with movement
- Nausea/vomiting
- Nasal congestion
- Feeling cold or warm
- Sensitive to smell/touch
- Neck pain
- Visual or other physical symptoms
- Other:_____

Potential triggers?
- Diet change
- Change in water/caffeine/alcohol intake
- Decreased sleep
- Medication change
- Increased stress
- Weather
- Amount of light
- Strong smells
- Loud sounds
- Hormone change
- Pressure on head
- Vitamin/mineral deficiency
- Change in exercise
- Travel
- Other:_____

Feelings afterward?
- Feel normal
- Depressed
- Very happy
- Fatigued
- Decreased concentration
- Other:_____

Additional details of headache:

Date:_____ Time:_____

How long did the headache last:_____

How severe is the pain? (Circle a number)

1   2   3   4   5   6   7   8   9   10

Warning signs (hours to days prior)?

- ◯ Mood change
- ◯ Decreased concentration
- ◯ Visual disturbance
- ◯ Physical symptoms
- ◯ Fatigue
- ◯ Sensitivity to light, sounds, or smells
- ◯ Neck discomfort
- ◯ Difficult speaking/reading
- ◯ Nausea
- ◯ Change in bowel habits
- ◯ Food cravings/thirst
- ◯ Yawning
- ◯ Other:_____

Headache symptoms?

- ◯ Pain on one side
- ◯ Pain on both sides
- ◯ Throbbing pain
- ◯ Constant pain
- ◯ Sensitive to light
- ◯ Sensitive to sound
- ◯ Worse with movement
- ◯ Nausea/vomiting
- ◯ Nasal congestion
- ◯ Feeling cold or warm
- ◯ Sensitive to smell/touch
- ◯ Neck pain
- ◯ Visual or other physical symptoms
- ◯ Other:_____

Potential triggers?

- ◯ Diet change
- ◯ Change in water/caffeine/alcohol intake
- ◯ Decreased sleep
- ◯ Medication change
- ◯ Increased stress
- ◯ Weather
- ◯ Amount of light
- ◯ Strong smells
- ◯ Loud sounds
- ◯ Hormone change
- ◯ Pressure on head
- ◯ Vitamin/mineral deficiency
- ◯ Change in exercise
- ◯ Travel
- ◯ Other:_____

Feelings afterward?

- ◯ Feel normal
- ◯ Depressed
- ◯ Very happy
- ◯ Fatigued
- ◯ Decreased concentration
- ◯ Other:_____

Additional details of headache:

Date:_____ Time:_____

How long did the headache last:_____

How severe is the pain? (Circle a number)

1   2   3   4   5   6   7   8   9   10

Warning signs (hours to days prior)?

Mood change
Decreased concentration
Visual disturbance
Physical symptoms
Fatigue
Sensitivity to light, sounds, or smells
Neck discomfort
Difficult speaking/reading
Nausea
Change in bowel habits
Food cravings/thirst
Yawning
Other:_____

Headache symptoms?

Pain on one side
Pain on both sides
Throbbing pain
Constant pain
Sensitive to light
Sensitive to sound
Worse with movement
Nausea/vomiting
Nasal congestion
Feeling cold or warm
Sensitive to smell/touch
Neck pain
Visual or other physical symptoms
Other:_____

Potential triggers?

Diet change
Change in water/caffeine/alcohol intake
Decreased sleep
Medication change
Increased stress
Weather
Amount of light
Strong smells
Loud sounds
Hormone change
Pressure on head
Vitamin/mineral deficiency
Change in exercise
Travel
Other:_____

Feelings afterward?

Feel normal
Depressed
Very happy
Fatigued
Decreased concentration
Other:_____

Additional details of headache:

Date:_____ Time:_____

How long did the headache last:_____

How severe is the pain? (Circle a number)

1 2 3 4 5 6 7 8 9 10

Warning signs (hours to days prior)?

- ○ Mood change
- ○ Decreased concentration
- ○ Visual disturbance
- ○ Physical symptoms
- ○ Fatigue
- ○ Sensitivity to light, sounds, or smells
- ○ Neck discomfort
- ○ Difficult speaking/reading
- ○ Nausea
- ○ Change in bowel habits
- ○ Food cravings/thirst
- ○ Yawning
- ○ Other:_____

Headache symptoms?

- ○ Pain on one side
- ○ Pain on both sides
- ○ Throbbing pain
- ○ Constant pain
- ○ Sensitive to light
- ○ Sensitive to sound
- ○ Worse with movement
- ○ Nausea/vomiting
- ○ Nasal congestion
- ○ Feeling cold or warm
- ○ Sensitive to smell/touch
- ○ Neck pain
- ○ Visual or other physical symptoms
- ○ Other:_____

Potential triggers?

- ○ Diet change
- ○ Change in water/caffeine/alcohol intake
- ○ Decreased sleep
- ○ Medication change
- ○ Increased stress
- ○ Weather
- ○ Amount of light
- ○ Strong smells
- ○ Loud sounds
- ○ Hormone change
- ○ Pressure on head
- ○ Vitamin/mineral deficiency
- ○ Change in exercise
- ○ Travel
- ○ Other:_____

Feelings afterward?

- ○ Feel normal
- ○ Depressed
- ○ Very happy
- ○ Fatigued
- ○ Decreased concentration
- ○ Other:_____

Additional details of headache:

Date:_____ Time:_____

How long did the headache last:_____

How severe is the pain? (Circle a number)

1   2   3   4   5   6   7   8   9   10

Warning signs (hours to days prior)?

Mood change
Decreased concentration
Visual disturbance
Physical symptoms
Fatigue
Sensitivity to light, sounds, or smells
Neck discomfort
Difficult speaking/reading
Nausea
Change in bowel habits
Food cravings/thirst
Yawning
Other:_____

Headache symptoms?

Pain on one side
Pain on both sides
Throbbing pain
Constant pain
Sensitive to light
Sensitive to sound
Worse with movement
Nausea/vomiting
Nasal congestion
Feeling cold or warm
Sensitive to smell/touch
Neck pain
Visual or other physical symptoms
Other:_____

Potential triggers?

Diet change
Change in water/caffeine/alcohol intake
Decreased sleep
Medication change
Increased stress
Weather
Amount of light
Strong smells
Loud sounds
Hormone change
Pressure on head
Vitamin/mineral deficiency
Change in exercise
Travel
Other:_____

Feelings afterward?

Feel normal
Depressed
Very happy
Fatigued
Decreased concentration
Other:_____

Additional details of headache:

Date:_____ Time:_____

How long did the headache last:_____

How severe is the pain? (Circle a number)

1   2   3   4   5   6   7   8   9   10

Warning signs (hours to days prior)?

- ○ Mood change
- ○ Decreased concentration
- ○ Visual disturbance
- ○ Physical symptoms
- ○ Fatigue
- ○ Sensitivity to light, sounds, or smells
- ○ Neck discomfort
- ○ Difficult speaking/reading
- ○ Nausea
- ○ Change in bowel habits
- ○ Food cravings/thirst
- ○ Yawning
- ○ Other:_____

Headache symptoms?

- ○ Pain on one side
- ○ Pain on both sides
- ○ Throbbing pain
- ○ Constant pain
- ○ Sensitive to light
- ○ Sensitive to sound
- ○ Worse with movement
- ○ Nausea/vomiting
- ○ Nasal congestion
- ○ Feeling cold or warm
- ○ Sensitive to smell/touch
- ○ Neck pain
- ○ Visual or other physical symptoms
- ○ Other:_____

Potential triggers?

- ○ Diet change
- ○ Change in water/caffeine/alcohol intake
- ○ Decreased sleep
- ○ Medication change
- ○ Increased stress
- ○ Weather
- ○ Amount of light
- ○ Strong smells
- ○ Loud sounds
- ○ Hormone change
- ○ Pressure on head
- ○ Vitamin/mineral deficiency
- ○ Change in exercise
- ○ Travel
- ○ Other:_____

Feelings afterward?

- ○ Feel normal
- ○ Depressed
- ○ Very happy
- ○ Fatigued
- ○ Decreased concentration
- ○ Other:_____

Additional details of headache:

Date:_____ Time:_____

How long did the headache last:_____

How severe is the pain? (Circle a number)

1   2   3   4   5   6   7   8   9   10

Warning signs (hours to days prior)?

- Mood change
- Decreased concentration
- Visual disturbance
- Physical symptoms
- Fatigue
- Sensitivity to light, sounds, or smells
- Neck discomfort
- Difficult speaking/reading
- Nausea
- Change in bowel habits
- Food cravings/thirst
- Yawning
- Other:_____

Headache symptoms?

- Pain on one side
- Pain on both sides
- Throbbing pain
- Constant pain
- Sensitive to light
- Sensitive to sound
- Worse with movement
- Nausea/vomiting
- Nasal congestion
- Feeling cold or warm
- Sensitive to smell/touch
- Neck pain
- Visual or other physical symptoms
- Other:_____

Potential triggers?

- Diet change
- Change in water/caffeine/alcohol intake
- Decreased sleep
- Medication change
- Increased stress
- Weather
- Amount of light
- Strong smells
- Loud sounds
- Hormone change
- Pressure on head
- Vitamin/mineral deficiency
- Change in exercise
- Travel
- Other:_____

Feelings afterward?

- Feel normal
- Depressed
- Very happy
- Fatigued
- Decreased concentration
- Other:_____

Additional details of headache:

Date:_____ Time:_____

How long did the headache last:_____

How severe is the pain? (Circle a number)

1 2 3 4 5 6 7 8 9 10

Warning signs (hours to days prior)?

- ○ Mood change
- ○ Decreased concentration
- ○ Visual disturbance
- ○ Physical symptoms
- ○ Fatigue
- ○ Sensitivity to light, sounds, or smells
- ○ Neck discomfort
- ○ Difficult speaking/reading
- ○ Nausea
- ○ Change in bowel habits
- ○ Food cravings/thirst
- ○ Yawning
- ○ Other:_____

Headache symptoms?

- ○ Pain on one side
- ○ Pain on both sides
- ○ Throbbing pain
- ○ Constant pain
- ○ Sensitive to light
- ○ Sensitive to sound
- ○ Worse with movement
- ○ Nausea/vomiting
- ○ Nasal congestion
- ○ Feeling cold or warm
- ○ Sensitive to smell/touch
- ○ Neck pain
- ○ Visual or other physical symptoms
- ○ Other:_____

Potential triggers?

- ○ Diet change
- ○ Change in water/caffeine/alcohol intake
- ○ Decreased sleep
- ○ Medication change
- ○ Increased stress
- ○ Weather
- ○ Amount of light
- ○ Strong smells
- ○ Loud sounds
- ○ Hormone change
- ○ Pressure on head
- ○ Vitamin/mineral deficiency
- ○ Change in exercise
- ○ Travel
- ○ Other:_____

Feelings afterward?

- ○ Feel normal
- ○ Depressed
- ○ Very happy
- ○ Fatigued
- ○ Decreased concentration
- ○ Other:_____

Additional details of headache:

Date:_____ Time:_____

How long did the headache last:_____

How severe is the pain? (Circle a number)

1 2 3 4 5 6 7 8 9 10

Warning signs (hours to days prior)?

- Mood change
- Decreased concentration
- Visual disturbance
- Physical symptoms
- Fatigue
- Sensitivity to light, sounds, or smells
- Neck discomfort
- Difficult speaking/reading
- Nausea
- Change in bowel habits
- Food cravings/thirst
- Yawning
- Other:_____

Headache symptoms?

- Pain on one side
- Pain on both sides
- Throbbing pain
- Constant pain
- Sensitive to light
- Sensitive to sound
- Worse with movement
- Nausea/vomiting
- Nasal congestion
- Feeling cold or warm
- Sensitive to smell/touch
- Neck pain
- Visual or other physical symptoms
- Other:_____

Potential triggers?

- Diet change
- Change in water/caffeine/alcohol intake
- Decreased sleep
- Medication change
- Increased stress
- Weather
- Amount of light
- Strong smells
- Loud sounds
- Hormone change
- Pressure on head
- Vitamin/mineral deficiency
- Change in exercise
- Travel
- Other:_____

Feelings afterward?

- Feel normal
- Depressed
- Very happy
- Fatigued
- Decreased concentration
- Other:_____

Additional details of headache:

Date:_____ Time:_____

How long did the headache last:_____

How severe is the pain? (Circle a number)

1   2   3   4   5   6   7   8   9   10

Warning signs (hours to days prior)?

- Mood change
- Decreased concentration
- Visual disturbance
- Physical symptoms
- Fatigue
- Sensitivity to light, sounds, or smells
- Neck discomfort
- Difficult speaking/reading
- Nausea
- Change in bowel habits
- Food cravings/thirst
- Yawning
- Other:_____

Headache symptoms?

- Pain on one side
- Pain on both sides
- Throbbing pain
- Constant pain
- Sensitive to light
- Sensitive to sound
- Worse with movement
- Nausea/vomiting
- Nasal congestion
- Feeling cold or warm
- Sensitive to smell/touch
- Neck pain
- Visual or other physical symptoms
- Other:_____

Potential triggers?

- Diet change
- Change in water/caffeine/alcohol intake
- Decreased sleep
- Medication change
- Increased stress
- Weather
- Amount of light
- Strong smells
- Loud sounds
- Hormone change
- Pressure on head
- Vitamin/mineral deficiency
- Change in exercise
- Travel
- Other:_____

Feelings afterward?

- Feel normal
- Depressed
- Very happy
- Fatigued
- Decreased concentration
- Other:_____

Additional details of headache:

Date:_____ Time:_____

How long did the headache last:_____

How severe is the pain? (Circle a number)

1   2   3   4   5   6   7   8   9   10

Warning signs (hours to days prior)?

Mood change
Decreased concentration
Visual disturbance
Physical symptoms
Fatigue
Sensitivity to light, sounds, or smells
Neck discomfort
Difficult speaking/reading
Nausea
Change in bowel habits
Food cravings/thirst
Yawning
Other:_____

Headache symptoms?

Pain on one side
Pain on both sides
Throbbing pain
Constant pain
Sensitive to light
Sensitive to sound
Worse with movement
Nausea/vomiting
Nasal congestion
Feeling cold or warm
Sensitive to smell/touch
Neck pain
Visual or other physical symptoms
Other:_____

Potential triggers?

Diet change
Change in water/caffeine/alcohol intake
Decreased sleep
Medication change
Increased stress
Weather
Amount of light
Strong smells
Loud sounds
Hormone change
Pressure on head
Vitamin/mineral deficiency
Change in exercise
Travel
Other:_____

Feelings afterward?

Feel normal
Depressed
Very happy
Fatigued
Decreased concentration
Other:_____

Additional details of headache:

Date:_____ Time:_____

How long did the headache last:_____

How severe is the pain? (Circle a number)

1 2 3 4 5 6 7 8 9 10

Warning signs (hours to days prior)?

- ○ Mood change
- ○ Decreased concentration
- ○ Visual disturbance
- ○ Physical symptoms
- ○ Fatigue
- ○ Sensitivity to light, sounds, or smells
- ○ Neck discomfort
- ○ Difficult speaking/reading
- ○ Nausea
- ○ Change in bowel habits
- ○ Food cravings/thirst
- ○ Yawning
- ○ Other:_____

Headache symptoms?

- ○ Pain on one side
- ○ Pain on both sides
- ○ Throbbing pain
- ○ Constant pain
- ○ Sensitive to light
- ○ Sensitive to sound
- ○ Worse with movement
- ○ Nausea/vomiting
- ○ Nasal congestion
- ○ Feeling cold or warm
- ○ Sensitive to smell/touch
- ○ Neck pain
- ○ Visual or other physical symptoms
- ○ Other:_____

Potential triggers?

- ○ Diet change
- ○ Change in water/caffeine/alcohol intake
- ○ Decreased sleep
- ○ Medication change
- ○ Increased stress
- ○ Weather
- ○ Amount of light
- ○ Strong smells
- ○ Loud sounds
- ○ Hormone change
- ○ Pressure on head
- ○ Vitamin/mineral deficiency
- ○ Change in exercise
- ○ Travel
- ○ Other:_____

Feelings afterward?

- ○ Feel normal
- ○ Depressed
- ○ Very happy
- ○ Fatigued
- ○ Decreased concentration
- ○ Other:_____

Additional details of headache:

Date:_____ Time:_____

How long did the headache last:_____

How severe is the pain? (Circle a number)

1   2   3   4   5   6   7   8   9   10

Warning signs (hours to days prior)?

- Mood change
- Decreased concentration
- Visual disturbance
- Physical symptoms
- Fatigue
- Sensitivity to light, sounds, or smells
- Neck discomfort
- Difficult speaking/reading
- Nausea
- Change in bowel habits
- Food cravings/thirst
- Yawning
- Other:_____

Headache symptoms?

- Pain on one side
- Pain on both sides
- Throbbing pain
- Constant pain
- Sensitive to light
- Sensitive to sound
- Worse with movement
- Nausea/vomiting
- Nasal congestion
- Feeling cold or warm
- Sensitive to smell/touch
- Neck pain
- Visual or other physical symptoms
- Other:_____

Potential triggers?

- Diet change
- Change in water/caffeine/alcohol intake
- Decreased sleep
- Medication change
- Increased stress
- Weather
- Amount of light
- Strong smells
- Loud sounds
- Hormone change
- Pressure on head
- Vitamin/mineral deficiency
- Change in exercise
- Travel
- Other:_____

Feelings afterward?

- Feel normal
- Depressed
- Very happy
- Fatigued
- Decreased concentration
- Other:_____

Additional details of headache:

Date:_____ Time:_____

How long did the headache last:_____

How severe is the pain? (Circle a number)

1 2 3 4 5 6 7 8 9 10

Warning signs (hours to days prior)?

- ○ Mood change
- ○ Decreased concentration
- ○ Visual disturbance
- ○ Physical symptoms
- ○ Fatigue
- ○ Sensitivity to light, sounds, or smells
- ○ Neck discomfort
- ○ Difficult speaking/reading
- ○ Nausea
- ○ Change in bowel habits
- ○ Food cravings/thirst
- ○ Yawning
- ○ Other:_____

Headache symptoms?

- ○ Pain on one side
- ○ Pain on both sides
- ○ Throbbing pain
- ○ Constant pain
- ○ Sensitive to light
- ○ Sensitive to sound
- ○ Worse with movement
- ○ Nausea/vomiting
- ○ Nasal congestion
- ○ Feeling cold or warm
- ○ Sensitive to smell/touch
- ○ Neck pain
- ○ Visual or other physical symptoms
- ○ Other:_____

Potential triggers?

- ○ Diet change
- ○ Change in water/caffeine/alcohol intake
- ○ Decreased sleep
- ○ Medication change
- ○ Increased stress
- ○ Weather
- ○ Amount of light
- ○ Strong smells
- ○ Loud sounds
- ○ Hormone change
- ○ Pressure on head
- ○ Vitamin/mineral deficiency
- ○ Change in exercise
- ○ Travel
- ○ Other:_____

Feelings afterward?

- ○ Feel normal
- ○ Depressed
- ○ Very happy
- ○ Fatigued
- ○ Decreased concentration
- ○ Other:_____

Additional details of headache:

Date:_____ Time:_____

How long did the headache last:_____

How severe is the pain? (Circle a number)

1   2   3   4   5   6   7   8   9   10

Warning signs (hours to days prior)?

- Mood change
- Decreased concentration
- Visual disturbance
- Physical symptoms
- Fatigue
- Sensitivity to light, sounds, or smells
- Neck discomfort
- Difficult speaking/reading
- Nausea
- Change in bowel habits
- Food cravings/thirst
- Yawning
- Other:_____

Headache symptoms?

- Pain on one side
- Pain on both sides
- Throbbing pain
- Constant pain
- Sensitive to light
- Sensitive to sound
- Worse with movement
- Nausea/vomiting
- Nasal congestion
- Feeling cold or warm
- Sensitive to smell/touch
- Neck pain
- Visual or other physical symptoms
- Other:_____

Potential triggers?

- Diet change
- Change in water/caffeine/alcohol intake
- Decreased sleep
- Medication change
- Increased stress
- Weather
- Amount of light
- Strong smells
- Loud sounds
- Hormone change
- Pressure on head
- Vitamin/mineral deficiency
- Change in exercise
- Travel
- Other:_____

Feelings afterward?

- Feel normal
- Depressed
- Very happy
- Fatigued
- Decreased concentration
- Other:_____

Additional details of headache:

Date:_____ Time:_____

How long did the headache last:_____

How severe is the pain? (Circle a number)

1   2   3   4   5   6   7   8   9   10

Warning signs (hours to days prior)?

- ◯ Mood change
- ◯ Decreased concentration
- ◯ Visual disturbance
- ◯ Physical symptoms
- ◯ Fatigue
- ◯ Sensitivity to light, sounds, or smells
- ◯ Neck discomfort
- ◯ Difficult speaking/reading
- ◯ Nausea
- ◯ Change in bowel habits
- ◯ Food cravings/thirst
- ◯ Yawning
- ◯ Other:_____

Headache symptoms?

- ◯ Pain on one side
- ◯ Pain on both sides
- ◯ Throbbing pain
- ◯ Constant pain
- ◯ Sensitive to light
- ◯ Sensitive to sound
- ◯ Worse with movement
- ◯ Nausea/vomiting
- ◯ Nasal congestion
- ◯ Feeling cold or warm
- ◯ Sensitive to smell/touch
- ◯ Neck pain
- ◯ Visual or other physical symptoms
- ◯ Other:_____

Potential triggers?

- ◯ Diet change
- ◯ Change in water/caffeine/alcohol intake
- ◯ Decreased sleep
- ◯ Medication change
- ◯ Increased stress
- ◯ Weather
- ◯ Amount of light
- ◯ Strong smells
- ◯ Loud sounds
- ◯ Hormone change
- ◯ Pressure on head
- ◯ Vitamin/mineral deficiency
- ◯ Change in exercise
- ◯ Travel
- ◯ Other:_____

Feelings afterward?

- ◯ Feel normal
- ◯ Depressed
- ◯ Very happy
- ◯ Fatigued
- ◯ Decreased concentration
- ◯ Other:_____

Additional details of headache:

Made in the USA
Monee, IL
11 April 2022

94547361R00115